Nature in the City

A Guide to Leading Nature Activities with Young People

Revised and Updated

The Cleveland Museum of Natural History

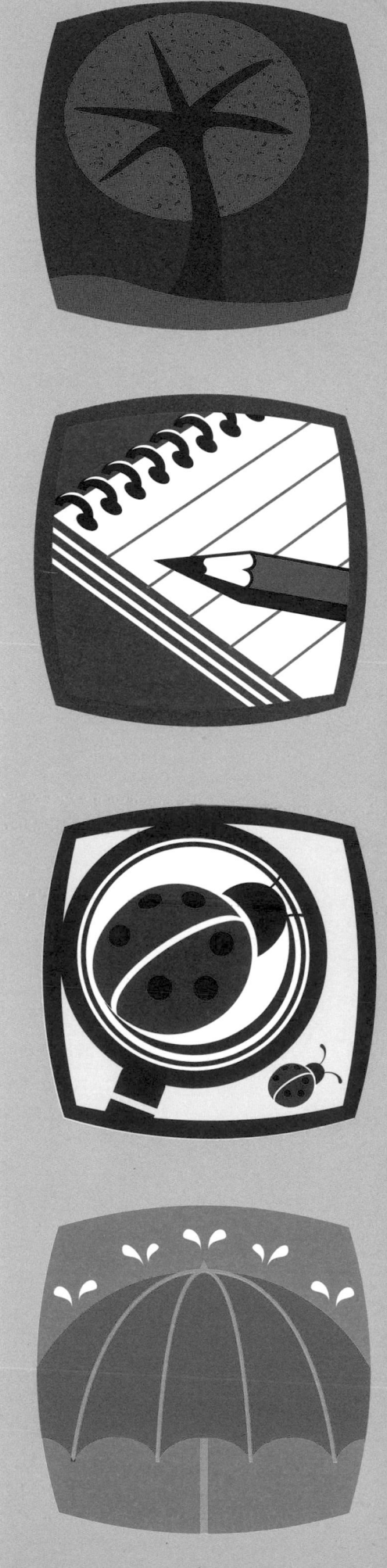

Cleveland Museum of
NATURAL HISTORY

Cleveland Museum of
NATURAL HISTORY

First Edition, 1979
Second Edition, 2017
ISBN-10: 0-692-83814-7
ISBN-13: 978-0-692-83814-3

Dedicated to Mary Lou Ferbert, whose love for the natural world — and passion for sharing it with others — inspired this project and continues to inspire us all.

Acknowledgments

This publication would not exist today without the hard work of dedicated individuals who compiled the original 1979 edition. These included:

- The volunteer staff of the Cleveland Museum of Natural History (CMNH) Environmental Information Service, who helped develop and edit the original *Nature in the City* Program: Frannie Newell, Peg McCreary and Diana Stromberg.
- Science specialists who ensured the scientific accuracy of the original text and teaching methods: Mary Flahive, Jim Bissell, David Konopka, Marti Long, Bob Segedi, Sonja Teraguchi and Harvey Webster — all staff members of the CMNH; and Peggy Archacki, Assistant Supervisor of Science of the Cleveland Board of Education.
- Those involved in the pilot project to develop the original program: the supervisors, classroom teachers and students of the following school districts: Cleveland, Cleveland Heights-University Heights and Lakewood; the evaluation team from The College of Education, Cleveland State University; and Mary Flahive, CMNH Curator of Education, and the CMNH science specialists.
- Original author and program originator: Mary Lou Ferbert, Coordinator, CMNH Environmental Information Service

This updated 2017 edition represents the significant efforts of the following:

- Renee Boronka, Associate Director, Natural Areas Program, CMNH, who coordinated the project
- Nancy Howell, Educator, CMNH, who reviewed the educational content
- Wendy Donkin, Graphic Designer and Illustrator
- Sarah Riehl, Writer and Editor
- Peter Chirdon, Volunteer, CMNH, who retyped the entire guide
- Wendy Wasman, Librarian and Archivist, CMNH, who created the Curriculum Resource Guide and proofread
- Trish Fox, Herbarium Coordinator, CMNH, who indexed the guide and proofread
- Judy Semroc, Naturalist, CMNH, who provided editorial input during the editing process
- Educators Rose Marie D'Amico and Sharon Doerge, who were instrumental in creating the original curriculum and who reviewed and commented on the early stages of this revision

Funding to reproduce *Nature in the City* was provided through donations to CMNH's Natural Areas Fund and by a grant from ArcelorMittal.

ArcelorMittal

On the Cover: *Milkweed at the Lumber Mill,* by Mary Lou Ferbert. Ferbert has spent her life sharing her passion for nature in her watercolor artwork and through projects such as the first edition of this Adventure Guide.

Cleveland Museum of
NATURAL HISTORY

Cleveland Museum of Natural History
1 Wade Oval Drive, University Circle
Cleveland, OH 44106
www.cmnh.org

Nature in the City

A Guide to Leading Nature Activities with Young People

Table of Contents

Introduction

Adventures

Foreword

I grew up on the near West Side of Cleveland during a time when playing outside was commonplace. My neighborhood friends and I met up on our street to climb trees, play kickball and run through sprinklers. I was a city kid, wise to the urban landscape around me.

But I was fortunate to have a father who liked to camp. He took our family on long respites from city life. We went places where we were immersed in nature. We hiked to beaver ponds, listened to insects and swam in lakes. From a young age, I was at ease in the outdoors and loved wild places as much as I did my home in the city.

I now work at the Museum. As part of my job, I lead field trips to local natural areas. I occasionally take city kids on these trips, and it has been eye-opening to realize how unfamiliar many of them are with nature.

I vividly recall taking a group of urban kids on a river walk and suggesting we wade in the water. They looked at me like I had two heads. Then a mild rainstorm hit. The kids were terrified, and went running back to the bus. Their fear took me aback.

A few years ago, Museum Curator of Botany and Natural Areas Program Director Jim Bissell shared a copy of the original *Nature in the City* Adventure Guide with me. It was developed in 1979 to introduce nature to urban youth in Cleveland by inviting them to explore a site nearby where they could observe natural processes at work. I was impressed at how forward-thinking the publication was, and I immediately decided it needed to be reprinted. Though parts here and there were showing their age, the majority of the curriculum still felt relevant and useful.

Over the last couple of years, I have worked with colleagues Nancy Howell, Sarah Riehl and Wendy Donkin to revise and update the Adventures in this guide. Our goal has been to rejuvenate the curriculum so that it remains true to its original intent, but reaches a broader audience. Whether you work with children formally or informally, or are a parent homeschooling or just looking for ways to spend quality time with your kids, this guide will help you lead nature experiences and science lessons that are simple, fun and informative. Significant parts of the Adventure Guide involve being outside. Any small outdoor area, such as an urban or suburban backyard or apartment courtyard, will do.

I am so pleased to bring this second edition of *Nature in the City* to print. I hope that it will provide a path by which more kids can encounter, feel at ease in and develop a love for the natural world. From personal experience, I can say that it's a gift that will last them a lifetime.

Happy trails,

Renee Schrift Boronka
Associate Director
Natural Areas & Botany
Cleveland Museum of Natural History

Mary Lou Ferbert

About Nature in the City

Mary Lou Ferbert has a message for teachers, parents and others setting out to use the *Nature in the City* Adventure Guide: "You don't have to have all the answers!"

It's all part of the plan with this curriculum, which she helped launch in the 1970s: Focus on having students appreciate the processes at work in the natural world and worry less about details like precise identifications and Latin names. This unique approach is the product of Ferbert's lifelong curiosity about the natural world and experience as a volunteer educator.

She traces the idea for *Nature in the City* back to a time in her life when she was deeply involved at the Museum, coordinating its Environmental Information Service and leading gallery tours and classes. Simultaneously, she was cultivating a career as an artist.

She had found creative inspiration in Cleveland's industrial Flats district, where she saw native plants reclaiming crumbling concrete and vacant lots. She was eager to share her discovery and, together with Museum Curator of Botany Jim Bissell, began leading field trips to the area for Museum members that showcased "nature in the city."

Ferbert was inspired to bring a similar experience to the children who lived in and around Cleveland. She collaborated with a small group of educators from the region's urban school districts, others who worked in the all-volunteer Environmental Information Service, and Museum science specialists to develop a curriculum that would be appropriate for grade-school children.

Together, they created an approach to nature education that doesn't require instructors to have any particular scientific background, simply an abiding curiosity. Adult leaders are encouraged to turn students' questions into learning opportunities. "If the students ask the name of something, ask them, 'Well, what name do you think it should have?' " Ferbert says.

Another curriculum goal is to help students tune in to the natural world that surrounds them at every turn. Ferbert realized the power that this could have as she observed students on a visit to their Field Site during the pilot phase of the curriculum.

"This young man started out sort of bored, not paying attention, and generally being very disruptive," she recalls. "Then he got turned on to some critter he found at the site, and he calmed down. He was focused and stopped disturbing the group." Having witnessed that transformation, Ferbert knew the curriculum was on the right track.

"We're setting the hook, and then letting the interest grow from there," she says.

Nature in the City was well-received, and requests for copies came from across the country. In testament to its sustained relevance, Museum donor ArcelorMittal expressed interest in funding a revision of the curriculum. This new edition introduces updated concepts where appropriate. It has also been adapted for use one-on-one with a child or by audiences outside the classroom, including home school families/groups, afterschool programs, and Scouting and other youth organizations.

It remains, however, true to the original curriculum's focus on the joy of discovery. As Ferbert emphasizes, "You want to get out there, nose to the ground, picking up bugs and plants and just having fun."

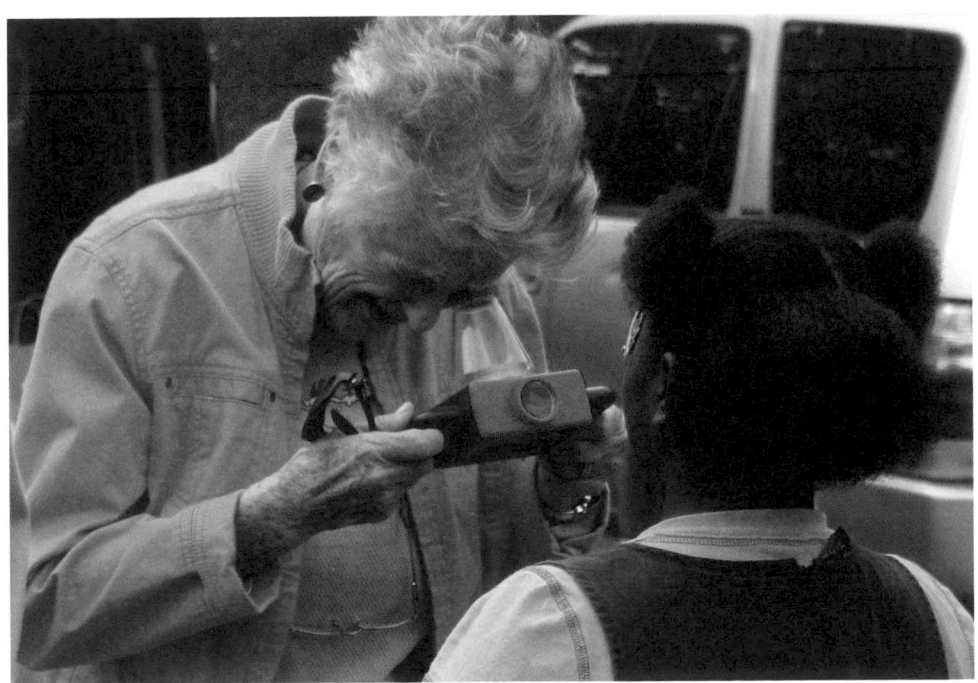

Mary Lou Ferbert, 2011

About this Adventure Guide

Nature in the City is a program designed by the Cleveland Museum of Natural History to introduce young people to the natural diversity that thrives in the urban world. Its goal is to build attitudes and values as participants increase their awareness, understanding and appreciation of the natural world. This program was developed to motivate young people to take an exciting field trip into their immediate environment and experience nature, instead of reading about it in textbooks. Although human activity has drastically altered the natural communities within our cities, a "vacant" lot, school yard, or backyard contains essentially the same lessons as a remote wilderness area.

This Adventure Guide provides a series of activities, many of them game-oriented, designed to heighten students' awareness of the natural world. Although it was written with third- to fifth-graders in mind, it can easily be adapted to any age group. The activities may be carried out on any natural spot of land within walking distance of your location (your "Field Site," as the guide calls it), perhaps even your own backyard! Learning to see the plants and animals that are present around you in a new context, and perhaps seeing them for the first time, can open the door to a whole new world filled with excitement and magic.

The Adventures presented here can be used as they are, or adapted to fit specific situations. However they are used, adult leaders are encouraged to take a relaxed approach that focuses on the thrill of discovery. As Richard Louv wrote in his book *Last Child in the Woods: Saving Our Children from Nature-Deficit Disorder*, "If getting our kids out into nature is a search for perfection, or is one more chore, then the belief in perfection and the chore defeats the joy. It's a good thing to learn more about nature in order to share this knowledge with children; it's even better if the adult and child learn about nature together. And it's a lot more fun."

Materials

The approach to learning presented in this Adventure Guide does not require an extensive knowledge of science, botany or natural history on the part of the leader or student. It involves only the desire to learn and the insight to say, "I don't know; let's look it up." Though addressed to the student, the Adventure Guide is intended for use by the adult leader. Additional information for this person, referred to as the Adventure Leader, is presented for each activity.

Specific instructional objectives for each Adventure are listed as "Missions" at the beginning of each unit. In addition, interdisciplinary goals appear in almost every Adventure.

Each Adventure has "Alternate Activities" to help you deal with inclement weather. We have tried to make these activities as interesting as the field-trip experience. As we have noted in the Adventure titled **BioBlitz!**, Alternate Activities can be excellent preparation for field trips to your Field Site.

Previous students using this program have enjoyed electing a "Plant of the Week" and a "Bug of the Week." We have also included a "Word of the Week." You'll find space for each of these at the end of each Adventure. We suggest that students also list these in the Field Journals that are an integral part of this curriculum. Words for "Word of the Week" may be taken from the text of the Adventure Guide or from words that students nominate that relate to their activities at the Field Site.

We call your attention to four activities that require observation or collecting over an extended period of time. They are: the Life Cycles activity on page 27 in **Common Denominators**; the Flying Contest activity on page 32 in **Weeds and Seeds**; the Tenant's Diary activity on page 38 in **Signs of the Season**; and **Create Change** on page 44. Read these Adventures ahead of time and start these activities as soon as possible to ensure the best learning experience. After you have familiarized yourself with the program, you will be able to decide how best to adapt them to your area and neighborhood situation.

Practicalities

The program is suitable for a variety of student situations. A homeschool student working with his or her parent should be able to carry out these activities as well as a small group of students in a classroom or afterschool enrichment program. If working with a group, ideally it should have 10 to 15 students. Obviously, most traditional classrooms exceed that number. In those cases, an adult assistant, if one is available, will be invaluable in helping to manage students outdoors.

We have tried to plan Adventures that can be accomplished in 45 minutes. However, if one 45-minute period is not practical, Adventures may be broken into smaller segments. If students are having a great time, Adventures may last longer!

We recommend the following:

- A notebook for each student that will serve as a Field Journal.

- A magnifying lens for discovering additional "mysteries" at the Field Site.

- Resource materials, such as books, brochures and websites for plant and animal identification at the Lab.

A word of caution concerning your outdoor activities: Be aware of the need for sun protection and be alert to possible mild or severe allergic reactions to plants and animals — for example, asthma or allergic reaction to insect stings. Also, be sure that you know the poisonous plants at your outdoor study site and are able to teach them to the students (e.g., poison ivy).

Tips

A few suggestions for maximizing your effectiveness at the outdoor study site:

- Check the Field Site and the route you'll use to get there before each visit to make some "discoveries" in advance. As soon as you leave to visit the Field Site, have all students be on the lookout for a "discovery." If no one finds something exciting, point out one of your own "discoveries," such as a plant that is growing in a crack in the pavement or the wall of a building. Have another "discovery" ready at the Field Site. If participants' attentions begin to stray, yet another "discovery" will help refocus them. Soon your students will be enthusiastically making their own discoveries. For example, students once found a dead mouse at their Field Site. The teacher, following nature's lead, had the wisdom to leave the animal where it lay. The group made regular observations on the decomposition process, one of the most important — and least understood — processes in nature.

- Discourage focusing on the question "What is it?" When students enthusiastically bring their discoveries for identification, ask them questions, such as "What do you think would be a good name for this plant?" or "How many legs does this animal have?" This program promotes active, not passive, learning. By showing your own curiosity, you will encourage the enthusiasm of your students and expand their curiosity.

- Use your time at the Field Site for experiencing nature. Look, smell, listen, touch. Save discussion and research for your Lab, which is your home base.

- Have fun! Your approach to the Field Site experience is the key to success. If you have fears or phobias, try not to influence your students with them. Perhaps this program will help change your feelings.

Working with Live Specimens

Through this program, the Cleveland Museum of Natural History hopes to nurture respect for nature. We can only accomplish this by raising everyone's awareness and understanding of nature.

Sometimes it is necessary to bring live animals into the classroom for close observation. These "guests" must be thoughtfully cared for, never abused, and returned to the place where they were collected. Opportunities for interesting discussions will arise as you plan how to handle and care for animals collected at the outdoor study site.

Occasionally collecting plant specimens also can enrich the classroom learning experience. The plant species that live in urban areas thrive on stress. Removing some –- or even several -– plants will not jeopardize the survival of these species. You, however, have the opportunity to shape your students' attitudes about collecting. Take only what you absolutely need. If there are many specimens of one kind of plant, collect one or two. If there is only one of a kind, leave it and make your observation at the site.

The activities in these Adventures should focus on fostering respect for all living things. Helping young people achieve a positive attitude about nature will benefit them as they go on to make decisions that affect the quality of life in tomorrow's world.

Summer Paris

A Mound STEM Elementary School (Cleveland Metropolitan School District) student uses a dual magnifier to look closely at a flower petal during a field trip to Mill Creek Falls (Cleveland Metroparks Garfield Park Reservation) in 2011.

Ready to get started?

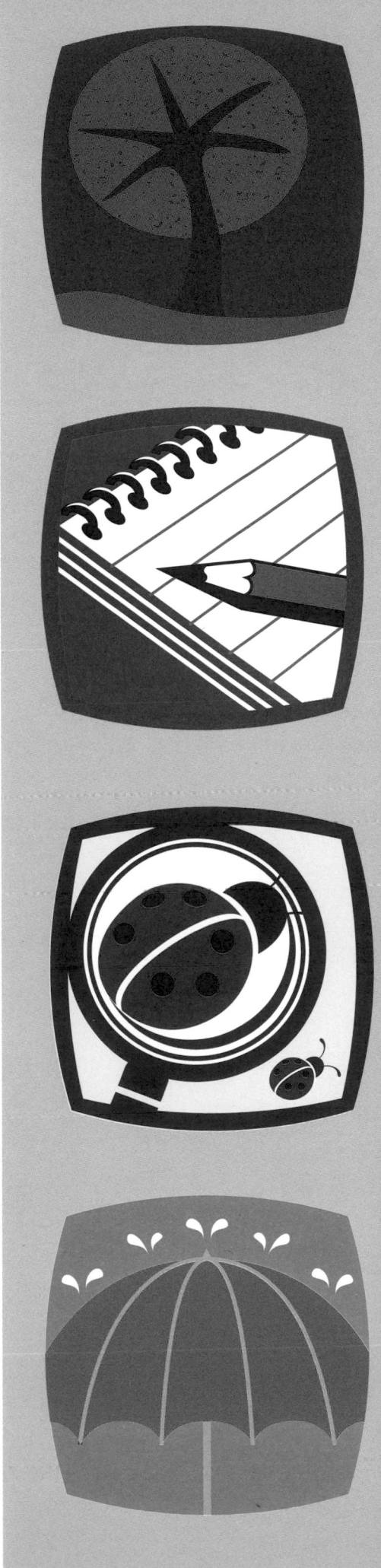

Set Your Sites! Resources

Burns, Loree Griffin. *Citizen Scientists: Be a Part of Scientific Discovery from Your Own Backyard.* New York: H. Holt, 2012.

Leslie, Clare Walker. *Keeping a Nature Journal: Discover a Whole New Way of Seeing the World Around You.* Pownal, VT: Storey Publishing, 2003.

Create Your Own Field Book Activity and Lesson Plan, from the Smithsonian's Field Book Project: www.mnh.si.edu/rc/field-books/education.html

Project NOAH (citizen science projects & photos): www.projectnoah.org

Supplies

Journal for each child

Notes

_____

_____

_____

_____

_____

_____

_____

_____

_____

_____

_____

_____

Set Your Sites!

Wild, Wonderful Words

adapt   frontier   potential
data   itinerary   site
environment

Explorers plan carefully.

Missions:

- To define a suitable Field Site by studying an imaginary one.
- To establish safety rules.
- To establish The Field Site Code of Conduct.
- To find a suitable Field Site.

Leader: Though it is desirable to get into the field as soon as possible, careful preparation for the outdoor experience is important for the success of the whole program as well as for everyone's safety. The time required for the preparation depends upon the readiness of your students.

 At the Lab

Leader: Introduce *Nature in the City.* Hand out journals. Explain to the students that they will explore an unknown frontier of their environment and find a new world.

Discussion

What are you curious about in nature? Take five minutes and write down three things from the natural world that you would like to have in your Field Site. Be able to tell why those are interesting to you.

Discuss the important things that should be present in a Field Site. List possible Field Sites and decide on the itinerary for your investigation of these sites. What are the potential dangers along the way? Plan how to deal with them.

Field Site Code of Conduct

Discuss the behavior required by activities outside the classroom. Decide what behavior will make "exploration" the safest, the most interesting and the most fun. If you are in a group, discuss the value of always using the "buddy system." Talk about ways in which we can show respect to nature, such as picking up litter when we see it or taking pictures of wildlife instead of disturbing it. Write your *Code of Conduct* in your journal.

On the Move

Now you are ready to go exploring and investigate different areas that would make a good Field Site.

Leader: Though it would be ideal for participants to help choose a site, this may not be possible. Be prepared to adapt the activities in this Adventure to your own situation.

 At the Lab

Discussion

Discuss each possible Field Site, keeping in mind what you decided were important characteristics. Select the most suitable area. You may need to obtain permission to use the site. For the duration of the program, the area you select will be called your "Field Site," and your classroom or examination area indoors will be your "Lab." You are urban explorers!

 Journal Activity

Plant of the Week: _____

Bug of the Week: _____

Word of the Week: _____

Word Review (fill in the blanks):

potential, itinerary

If we have decided that there are several _____ Field Sites nearby, we must plan the route we will follow to investigate those locations and write our _____.

frontiers, environment

In our own _____, we explorers can still find new _____.

Mapping the Territory Resources

Gatty, Harold. *Finding Your Way Without Map or Compass.* Mineola, NY: Dover Publications, 1999.

Gooley, Tristan. *The Natural Navigator: The Rediscovered Art of Letting Nature Be Your Guide.* New York: Experiment, 2012.

Kjellstrom, Bjorn. *Be Expert with Map and Compass.* 3rd ed. Hoboken, NJ: Wiley, 2010.

Cornell Lab of Ornithology YardMap project: yardmap.org/

Map Skills for Elementary Students from National Geographic: education.nationalgeographic.com/education/map-skills-elementary-students/

Supplies

Directional compass

Paper, pencils

Tape measure (helpful but not required)

Mapping the Territory

Wild, Wonderful Words

approximation	differentiate	relative	specific
cardinal directions	irregularities	route	symbol
compass	landmarks	scale	terrain
compass rose	pace	similarities	territory

Explorers have to know the territory.

Missions:
- To find the best route to your Field Site.
- To map the territory.

 ## At the Lab

Discussion
What route should you take to your Field Site? What are the possible dangers along your route? Be sure you know how to deal with them. Before you leave the Lab, review your Field Site Code of Conduct.

Map-Making Practice
How much do you know about making a map? A map is a special kind of drawing that represents an area. It tells you where things are located in relation to other things. A map will not be as big as the area it represents. Instead, map-makers use a scale for drawing maps. Practice map-making by drawing a map of your classroom or a room in your house.

Using a compass, determine which direction is north. Establish the other three cardinal directions. Put a compass rose in the corner of your map, positioned according to what the compass indicates. Does anyone know ways to determine north, south, east and west without a compass?

Discuss how you will go about making a map of your Field Site. Remember, you will have trees, bushes, fences, buildings, etc., to represent. How will you differentiate between them? What symbols will you use? Don't forget that you must establish north, south, east and west on the map of your Field Site.

DeAnna MacKeigan

Leader: Being able to establish the location of things is a part of scientific investigation. Actual measurements are not necessary for the success of this Adventure. Approximations are sufficient. Have the students measure the length and width of the room in paces. Assign a unit of measure, a centimeter or half-inch, to each pace. Draw lines of appropriate length for each wall of the room. By pacing, establish the size and placement of the doors and windows. Do the same for the room's furniture, making sure the students understand that they are to represent the furniture according to its relative size.

 ## At the Field Site

Sketch a map of the Field Site after pacing off the outer boundaries and the distances between important landmarks.

If you are working in a group, divide into teams. Take 10 minutes to search for objects that you have discussed at the Lab. Remember them so that you can make a list when you return to the Lab.

 ## At the Lab

Mapping
Make a final map of the route you take to the Field Site. Make a final map of the Field Site. Discuss the possible danger areas you discovered on the route, as well as at the Field Site, and include them on your maps if you like. Potential danger areas could be a yellowjacket nest or a patch of poison ivy. Post these maps at the Lab.

Code of Conduct
Have you found any changes you need to make in the Field Site Code of Conduct? If so, make them.

Memory Contest
If you are working in a group, divide into teams. Create lists of all the things you saw at the Field Site that you discussed before your visit. Be as specific as you can. If you don't know the name of something that you observed, draw it as well as you can. Whichever team has the longest list of correct answers wins the Memory Contest.

 ## Alternate Activity

Working in pairs, measure the length of each other's paces. Use that information to find the actual length of room in feet or meters. Compare results.

Word Review (fill in the blanks):

symbols, differentiate

By making up your own system of _____, we can draw a map of the Field Site and _____ between trees, fences and buildings.

pace, scale

If we use one centimeter to represent a _____, we can draw a map to _____.

irregularities, aware, terrain

Because of _____ in the _____, we have to be _____ of where we are walking when we go to the Field Site.

Journal Activity

Plant of the Week: _____

Bug of the Week: _____

Word of the Week: _____

BioBlitz!

Wild, Wonderful Words

alternate	invertebrate	mammal	vertebrate
inventory	litter	tenant	

Observation is the key to understanding. Let's go out and look!

Missions:
- To increase powers of observation through close examination of a Field Site.
- To discover that an urban spot is a good place to study nature.
- To discover that materials in human-made objects were originally part of nature.

 **At the Lab**

Identification Practice

Choose a plant, bird, mammal and invertebrate that you think may be present at your Field Site. Discuss which characteristics will help you identify it. (Examples: Plant: size, opposite or alternate leaves, shape of leaves, flower size, color and shape, if present, seed size, color and shape, if present. Bird: size, color and markings. Invertebrate: size, color, number of body parts, number of legs, where legs attach to body, where eyes are located.)

 At the Field Site

BioBlitz

A BioBlitz is an event that is held to find and identify all the living things in a certain area. Today, you are going to hold your own BioBlitz at your Field Site. If you have a group, divide into teams, or do this individually:

1. Find as many different objects as you can that are human-made. (Examples: glass, brick, fence, trash.) Make a team list of all these items. Some of you may want to draw pictures of them.

2. Find as many different animals as you can that live in or visit the Field Site. Make a list. If you cannot identify some of the animals, draw pictures that will help you look them up in the field guides at the Lab, paying particular attention to the characteristics necessary for identification.

3. Find as many different plants as you can that are growing at the Field Site. Follow the same directions as #2.

If you did find and record the trash or litter at your site, clean up what you can, safely. (Careful if there is broken glass or sharp pieces of metal.)

BioBlitz! Resources

Belwood, Jacqueline Janine. *In Ohio's Backyard: Bats.* Columbus: Ohio Biological Survey, 1998.

Bradley, Richard Alan. *In Ohio's Backyard: Spiders.* Columbus: Ohio Biological Survey, 2004.

Davis, Jeffrey G. *In Ohio's Backyard: Frogs and Toads.* Columbus: Ohio Biological Survey, OH, 2002.

FitzSimmons, David. *Animals of Ohio's Ponds and Vernal Pools.* Kent, OH: Kent State University Press, 2011.

Pfingsten, Ralph A., et al. *Amphibians of Ohio.* Columbus: Ohio Biological Survey, 2013.

Rosche, Larry, O., Judy M. Semroc, and Linda K. Gilbert. *Dragonflies and Damselflies of Northeast Ohio.* Cleveland: Cleveland Museum of Natural History, 2008.

Ohio Department of Natural Resources Species Guides: wildlife.ohiodnr.gov/species-and-habitats/species-guide-index

Plants: plants.usda.gov

Wildflowers: naturepreserves.ohiodnr.gov/natural-features-of-ohio/ohios-wildflowers

www.westernpawildflowers.com

Mosses and Lichens: ohiomosslichen.org/

Trees: www.arborday.org/trees/whatTree/

Insects: www.insectidentification.org/

Butterflies and Moths: www.butterfliesandmoths.org

www.wisconsinbutterflies.org

Birds: www.allaboutbirds.org

Mammals: naturalhistory.si.edu/mna

Spiders: osumarion.osu.edu/SpiderWeb/

Supplies

Paper, pencils, markers or crayons

Poster board

Trash bags

_____
_____
_____
_____
_____
_____
_____
_____
_____
_____
_____
_____
_____
_____
_____
_____
_____
_____
_____
_____
_____
_____

At the Lab

Field Site Inventory

Make a Field Site inventory from the results of your BioBlitz. Enter the list in your journal. Add to it as you find new plants and animals.

Discussion

What animals and plants might be present at the Field Site but hidden from view? Which animals might pass through the site but not stay?

What materials were used to make the objects observed in #1? (If you don't know, use a dictionary or the internet.) Did these materials come from nature?

Alternate Activity

Drawing from Nature

Using a large sheet of poster board or other paper, create a mural of your field site. For every natural item on your mural, try to include a human-made item.

Journal Activity

Plant of the Week: _____

Bug of the Week: _____

Word of the Week: _____

Word Review (fill in the blanks):

inventory, invertebrates, mammals

When we _____ our Field Site, we can group the Field Site tenants in the following categories: _____, plants, birds and _____.

data, tenants

When we record facts about the Field Site _____, we are collecting specific _____ over a period of time and keeping notes in our Field Site journals.

Nature Detectives

Wild, Wonderful Words

baiting	conscious	evidence	scavenger
burrow	decay	gnawing	speculate
clues	decomposed	mucous	techniques
component	droppings	recycle	

Good detective work is important in understanding animals. Look for clues that tell you not only that they exist but also how they exist.

Missions:

- To discover that the presence of an animal can be detected without observing the animal itself.
- To practice identifying animals from animal evidence.
- To learn baiting techniques useful in collecting animal evidence.
- To become more comfortable in handling, caring for and observing live insects and other invertebrates.
- To speculate about what happens to animal evidence.
- To discover that human beings are animals.
- To become more conscious of the growing problem of human litter and what individuals can do to help the situation.

 At the Lab

Discussion

During this visit to the Field Site, you will be looking for animal evidence, rather than animals themselves. Discuss what kinds of evidence you may see at your Field Site. (Review your Field Site inventory to jump-start your discussion.) Group examples under the following major categories:

- Animal homes (Examples: nest, burrow, web)
- Parts of an animal's body (Examples: bone, fur, feather, discarded skin)
- Droppings
- Tracks
- Evidence of animal activity (Examples: webs, mucous trails, partly eaten plant or animal material, holes, scratches or gnaw marks)

After the discussion, make a chart for "The Search." There should be a column on the chart for each of the five major categories above.

Animal homes	Parts of animals	Droppings	Tracks	Evidence of activity

Nature Detectives Resources

Eder, Tamara. *Animal Tracks of Ohio.* Renton, WA: Lone Pine Publishing, 2001.

Murie, Olaus J. and Mark A. Elbroch. *A Field Guide to Animal Tracks.* Peterson Field Guide Series. Boston: Houghton Mifflin Harcourt, 2005.

Sheldon, Ian. *Animal Tracks of the Great Lakes.* Renton, WA: Lone Pine Publishing, 1997.

Stokes, Donald W. and Lillian Q. Stokes. *A Guide to Animal Tracking and Behavior.* Boston: Little, Brown and Company, 1986.

Tracks and Signs: www.biokids.umich. edu/guides/tracks_and_sign/

Species Info for Kids: www.biokids. umich.edu

Bird feeding:www.feederwatch.org/ learn/feeding-birds/

Notes

_____

_____

_____

_____

_____

_____

_____

_____

_____

_____

 At the Field Site

The Search

Look for animal evidence. Record what you find in the proper column on your chart.

Detective Work

The following is a list of useful techniques for observing and collecting insects and other invertebrates:

- Leave a yellow bowl with water in a partially sunny spot.
- Paint honey or molasses on a tree.
- Hide old fruit or anything sugary among the plants.
- Bury a bowl so that its top is level with the surface of the ground. (You have made a pitfall trap.) Add a piece of banana or beer to make the bowl even more attractive. Cover with a piece of wood propped up by small stones.
- Smooth out the dirt in one area and bait with food, or bait after a fresh snowfall. Look for tracks.
- If you have dead trees, peel away some of the bark and see what's underneath.
- Observe visitors to blooming flowers.

Check the baits as early as possible the next day. Note the number, kind and direction of any animal tracks. Draw pictures of them. Look for insects and other invertebrates in the water trap, on the tree, on the fruit, in the pitfall trap and around the baits on the ground. Collect in a container a sample of each kind of insect. (Possible containers: plastic food container, zip-seal baggie. Do not use glass. Don't forget that animals need air. Either poke tiny holes in the lid of the container or secure fabric over the opening of a container with a rubber band.)

Place bird seed feeders or hummingbird feeders at your Field Site.

Plan on returning your animals to the Field Site after a period of observation.

For the very adventurous, set up a nighttime light trap. It's as simple as placing a white sheet or blanket out on a fence. Ideally, you should shine a light on the sheet. You'll be amazed at what you see in the morning!

Supplies

Zip-seal baggies

Small plastic bowl, such as reused margarine or yogurt container

Misc. baits

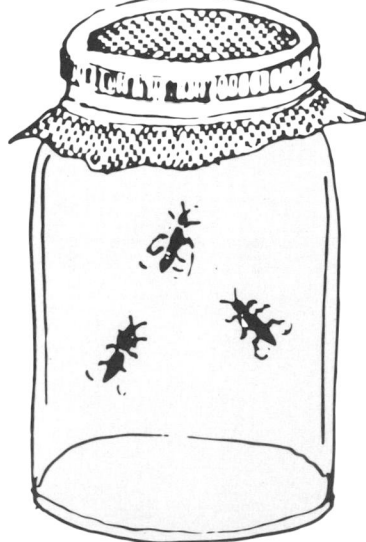

Helpful Tip

Save your empty plastic jar for a useful temporary home for observing animals.

 **At the Lab**

Discussion

What will happen to each item of animal evidence that you have listed on your charts? (Examples: the wind blows away fur and feathers, rain erases tracks, animal wastes decay to become a component of the soil.)

Did you find any litter at the Field Site? Is litter animal evidence? Look up the word "animal" in the dictionary. Are you an animal? Remember to pick up any litter you find and dispose of it properly.

Leader: Point out that human beings are mammals and therefore are members of the animal kingdom.

Do you remember any evidence that a human being has visited your Field Site? Did you include human evidence on the team chart? What will happen to this evidence? Is there anything you can do about human litter? Consider the 4 R's: Rethink, Reduce, Reuse and Recycle.

Leader: Discuss the relative time for the natural decay of solid waste. Cans will not be completely decomposed for 100 years, aluminum for 400 years, 4,000-year-old glass has been found in archaeological excavations. Plastic pollution such as bags and bottles never really goes "away," it simply breaks down into smaller pieces.

Follow-up Detective Work

Try to identify the animal tracks you have drawn and the animals you have collected. If any of these animals are not already on your Field Site inventory, add them.

 Alternate Activity

Creative Cartoon

Using clues from your detective work, draw a cartoon strip in your journal that tells a story about one of the animals that visited the bait.

 **Journal Activity**

Plant of the Week: _____

Bug of the Week: _____

Word of the Week: _____

Word Review (fill in the blanks):

evidence, speculate

If we have collected data and think we have enough _____ ,
we can _____ about what will happen in the future.

gnawed, droppings, bait

If we set out _____ and come back later to find that
some animal has _____ it, we then have to make a detailed
study of all the evidence, such as tracks or _____ , so
that we can eliminate some of our guesses and perhaps find out
exactly what animal visited the Field Site.

clues, techniques, baiting

Using the _____ we have learned for _____ ,
perhaps we can find some _____ that will tell us what
animals visit the Field Site when we are not there.

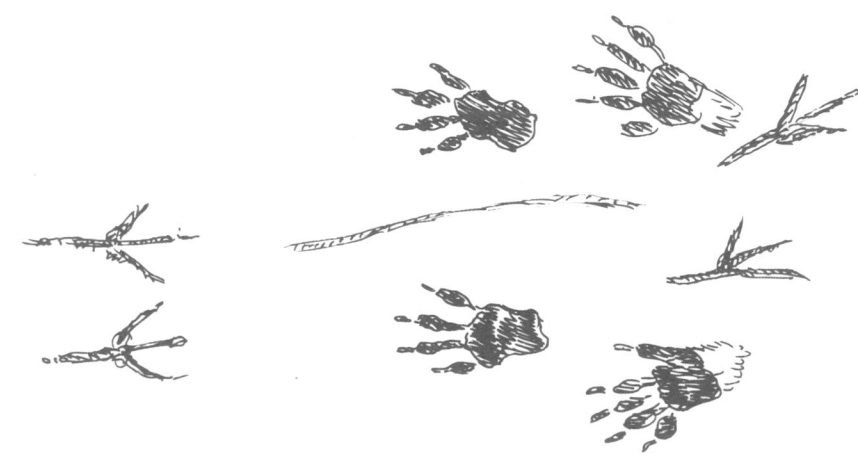

Moving Along

Wild, Wonderful Words

biomimicry	estimate	nocturnal	stalking
contracting	hibernate	research	sustainable
darting	locomotion	segments	varied
diurnal	migrate	soaring	vegetation

Almost all animals are able to move by themselves.

Missions:
- To develop habits of careful and detailed observation.
- To become more conscious of how, where, why and when animals move.

 **At the Field Site**

Observation

What moves? Choose one of the animals at your Field Site to study. Write your answers to the following questions in your journal. Make careful observations so that you will be prepared to play the game at the end of this adventure.

How does it move? What body parts does it use to move?

- **Legs**. Does your animal have legs? How many legs does the animal have? (Examples: human, bird, 2; dog, squirrel, 4; ant, beetle, butterfly, 6; spider, 8; sowbug, 14; millipede, many.) How do these legs move? Do they move together? (Examples: bird hopping, dog running.) Do they move forward alternately? (Examples: bird, girl, dog walking.) Do they move independently? (Examples: spider, ant.) When the animal moves faster or more slowly, does the pattern of leg movement change? How?

  Check for animal tracks in mud or snow. If you find any, try to identify the animal from its tracks and estimate the speed at which it was moving. See the Resources section in the sidebar for books and websites that can help.

- **Wings**. Does your animal have wings? Observe its flight. What kind of motion does it have in flight? (Examples: gliding/soaring, steady flapping, darting.) Where are the wings when it is not flying? Have you seen a butterfly resting? A moth? How are their wings positioned when they are resting?

- **Other Ways of Moving**. Observe the motion of an animal that uses neither legs nor wings to move. How does it move? (Example: a worm moves by contracting its body segments.)

Where does it move?

In the air, on vegetation, on the ground, in the soil or in the water? Does it use different body parts for motion if it moves in more than one of these places?

Moving Along Resources

Benyus, Janine M. *Biomimicry: Innovation Inspired by Nature.* New York: Perennial, 2002.

Cooke, John A. L. *The Restless Kingdom: An Exploration of Animal Movement.* New York: Facts on File, 1991.

Prince, J. H. *How Animals Move.* New York: Elsevier/Nelson Books, 1981.

Great Lakes Biomimicry: glbiomimicry.org/

Watch a short video about biomimicry: youtu.be/QpEsb-fun44

Why does it move?

Watch your animal and try to imagine why it is moving. (Examples: hunger, protection, comfort, shelter.) Does it move in a special way that tells you this?

When does it move?

- Day or night? Animals you see moving about your Field Site in the daytime are diurnal. Those that move at night are nocturnal. From your detective work in **Nature Detectives**, did you discover nocturnal animals that visited your Field Site? (Examples: opossum, raccoon.)

- In summer, fall, winter or spring? Are there animals that don't move, or that you don't see, during one of these seasons? Do some animals leave the area (migrate)? (Examples: Common Grackle, American Robin, Monarch Butterfly.) Do some animals sleep through winter (hibernate)? (Examples: fly, sowbug, spider, queen hornet and queen bumblebee.)

 ## At the Lab

Charades

Make or section off a simple runway. Take turns moving down the runway imitating the way your animal moves. At the end of the runway, stop and imitate the way the animal looks when it is not moving. The other students or your Adventure Leader can ask questions, to which you may only answer "yes" or "no." The goal is to guess, in 20 questions or less, what animal you are imitating.

 ## Alternate Activity

Leader: This activity can be done as a research project. Each student should do the research for one animal from their Field Site inventory and share his or her findings with the class or Adventure Leader. Sometimes students will be able to check their conclusions about animal motion by actual observation when the weather improves.

The Notion of Motion

Biomimicry looks to nature for ideas that can improve human life in a sustainable way. Think about how animal and plant motion has given people ideas for things that we use every day. One example is Velcro, which was inspired by the way burrs stick to an animal's fur and are transported from place to place. Draw a car, airplane, or other form of transport that borrows an idea from animal or plant movement.

 **Journal Activity**

Plant of the Week: _____

Bug of the Week: _____

Word of the Week: _____

Word Review (fill in the blanks):

migrate, nocturnal, hibernate, diurnal

Some animals are active during the day; they are called

_____ animals. Others are active during the night, or

_____. Animals respond differently to the seasons.

Some _____, that is, they travel to find the best climate for

their needs. Others _____, resting until better weather

returns.

varied, alternate, locomotion

Some animals have _____ means of _____.

Most birds _____ between using their wings and using

their legs to move from place to place.

contract, segments

You will have fun pretending that your body is made up of many

_____ that _____ to make you move if you

are crawling down the runway imitating a worm.

Sense and Nonsense Resources

Cole, Joanna. *The Magic School Bus Explores the Senses.* New York: Scholastic Press, 2001.

Hickman, Pamela. *Animal Senses: How Animals See, Hear, Taste, Smell and Feel.* Toronto: Kids Can Press, 1998.

Morton, Eugene S. and Jake Page. *Animal Talk: Science and the Voices of Nature.* New York: Random House, 1992.

Rogers, Lesley J. and Gisela Kaplan. *Songs, Roars, and Rituals: Communication in Birds, Mammals, and Other Animals.* Cambridge, MA: Harvard University Press, Cambridge, 2002.

Showers, Paul. *The Listening Walk.* Reprint ed. New York: HarperCollins, 1993.

Take a Walk and Explore Nature with Your Senses: simplekids.net/nature-walk-2/

Supplies

Bandana or scarf for blindfold

Something fragrant to hide

Sense and Nonsense

Wild, Wonderful Words

edible	roles	stagnant	vegetation
noise pollution	sense	textured	

You can use your eyes to see what is happening at your Field Site. Now use your other senses to make observations.

Mission:

- To develop powers of observation through the senses of touch, smell and hearing by eliminating the sense of sight.

We use our five senses to understand and interact with the world around us. Each of our senses gives us a different piece of information about our surroundings. It's up to our brains to put this information together, like pieces of a puzzle, so that we can completely understand what we're studying. Sight is a very important sense, but our other senses are powerful too, each in its own way.

 ## At the Field Site

Buddy System

At the Field Site, work with your Adventure Leader or, if in a group, divide into teams of two. One of you, with blindfold or eyes closed, will be guided by your "buddy." Then you will trade places. This activity requires trust between the team members. What would you like your buddy to warn you about when he or she is guiding you?

The blindfolded member of the team experiences things that are familiar using senses other than sight. (Examples: Sense of touch — rough-textured brick or piece of wood, smooth plastic, two leaves of different shape, the temperature in sun or shade. Sense of smell — mint leaf, stagnant water.)

With a little thought, a good guide can find many ways to utilize his or her buddy's sense of touch and smell. The guide and the blindfolded member of the team then switch roles.

The Sounds of Silence

Sit cross-legged on the ground in a circle, placing your elbows on your knees. Close your eyes. Make fists. For every different city sound that you hear, raise one finger on your right hand; for every different nature sound that you hear, raise one finger on your left hand. Your Adventure Leader will signal the end of two minutes. The person with the most fingers raised must then identify each sound represented by his or her fingers. The winners are the people who have heard and identified the most sounds.

Discuss the fact that too much noise becomes a type of pollution. Noise pollution can cause problems for people and wildlife. In people it can increase stress. Noise pollution causes animals to change where and when they migrate, hunt, hibernate and raise their young.

 At the Lab

Discussion

Have each member of the group tell about his or her most interesting sense experience during this Adventure — touching, smelling or hearing. What would your life be like if you used these senses more every day?

You probably didn't include the sense of taste. Why not? Are all plants edible? What plants do you know that are edible? What part of the plant is edible? Do you know the names of some plants that are not?

 Alternate Activities

Sense-ible Writing

In your journal, write a description of a natural object using as many of your senses as possible. Include as much detail as you can about what each sense can tell you. If you want, put your description in the form of a poem.

Sniff and Seek

Cover your eyes and have your Adventure Leader hide a strongly scented item such as a bouquet of lavender or a fresh loaf of bread somewhere in the room. Can you find it using just your sense of smell?

Grandma Schrift's Homemade Bread

In mixing bowl, combine:
 1 cup warm milk
 2 tablespoons butter, melted
 Use a kitchen thermometer to ensure mixture is between 105 and 115° F.

Add:
 2 tablespoons sugar
 3/4 teaspoon salt
 1 packet (2¼ teaspoons) active dry yeast

Let mixture sit for 6 minutes.

Add:
 2½ to 3 cups flour

Beat dough with dough hook on electric mixer (or knead by hand) until you can shape it into a ball. Add a bit of oil to a large bowl. Place dough in bowl and cover with a dish towel. Allow to rise for 2 to 2½ hours. Punch down a bit and allow to rise again for 1 hour. Punch down again and place dough in loaf pan. Allow to rise in the pan for 1 hour. Bake at 350° F for 30 minutes. Optional: Pour 1 tablespoon melted butter on top prior to baking or brush bread with butter after removing from the oven.

_____
_____
_____
_____
_____
_____
_____
_____
_____
_____
_____
_____
_____
_____
_____
_____
_____
_____
_____
_____
_____
_____
_____
_____

Animal Senses

What do animals use to tell what is around them? Locate photographs or find pictures on websites of a variety of animals (remember, "animal" was defined in **Nature Detectives**). Determine what sense or senses the animal would be best at using.

 Journal Activity

Plant of the Week: _____

Bug of the Week: _____

Word of the Week: _____

Word Review (fill in the blanks):

differentiate, textures, sense

If we use our _____ of touch, we can learn to _____ between objects when we become familiar with their _____ .

vegetation, edible

Plant-eating animals are interested only in _____ . While they search for their favorite plants, they must watch out for the meat-eaters that might consider them _____ .

What sense do you think this fox is best at using?

Lunch

Wild, Wonderful Words

carrion	food chain	objectives	shoots
complications	food pyramid	organic	sources
concept	food web	predator	
cultivated	nectar	prey	

A grasshopper eats a leaf. The grasshopper in turn is eaten by a mouse, and the mouse becomes food for a snake. If the snake is not careful, it can become food for a Great-horned Owl.

Missions:
- To become acquainted with the idea of a food chain.
- To become aware of how animals protect themselves from becoming another animal's lunch.
- To become aware of the sources of the food people eat.

Leader: To be an effective learning experience, Lunch Tag, the primary activity within this Adventure, requires a group of children to participate. If you are working with only one or two children, please review the Discussion and Alternate Activity sections for ideas to use.

 ## At the Lab

Discussion
Talk about what you normally eat for lunch. Consider the following: What is the natural source of this food? Are you eating plants or animals? Does this food come from nearby or far away? Do any of your neighbors grow or raise the animals for this food in their yards or in a community garden? Do they keep chickens or bees in their yards? Did the food for your lunch come from a grocery store? Is that grocery store nearby or far away?

Lunch Tag Preparation
Prepare to play Lunch Tag at your Field Site to better understand the eating habits and feeding relationships of animals.

In Lunch Tag, you will be acting out one specific food chain. The food chain includes the following: leaves, grasshopper, mouse, snake and Great-horned Owl. Each of you will play the role of one of the animals. Your objective is to "eat" without being "eaten" out of the game.

- Divide into two groups. Spend time discussing what food and how much food you think a grasshopper eats. How many grasshoppers do you think a mouse will eat for "lunch"? How many mice will a snake eat, etc.? Will you need more grasshoppers or more owls for a good food chain?

Lunch Resources

Dennis, John V. *Beyond the Bird Feeder: The Habits and Behavior of Feeding-Station Birds When They are Not at Your Feeder.* New York: Knopf, 1981.

Kalman, Bobbie. *What are Food Chains and Webs?* New York: Crabtree Publishing Company, 1998.

Kapchinske, Pam. *Hey Diddle Diddle: A Food Chain Tale.* Pleasant, SC: Sylvan Dell Publishing, 2011.

Lauber, Patricia. *Who Eats What? Food Chains and Food Webs.* New York: HarperCollins, 1994.

Food Chain Stacking Cups: funfamilycrafts.com/food-chain-stacking-cups/

Food Chain from National Geographic Education: www.nationalgeographic.org/encyclopedia/food-chain/

Food Chain and Food Web: www.ducksters.com/science/ecosystems/food_chain_and_web.php

---

Supplies
Chart

Markers/pencil

Paper

Whistle or bell (or other signal for Food Chain Game)

• Now decide how many of each kind of animal in the food chain should be in the game. How do these animals protect themselves from their enemies? Do they have a place of protection? Fill out the first three columns of the Animal Food Chain Chart.

Leader: See the Resources section of this guide for books and websites that can help you determine what each animal eats. Please note that complications arise if you allow the animals to eat other than their assigned foods (for example, letting the owl eat the mouse). You have then moved from the concept of food chain to that of food web. For this portion of the Adventure, avoid these complications by staying within the assigned food relationships.

• Choose animal-role assignments by lottery. Make a slip for each grasshopper, mouse, snake and owl that you plan to have in the game. Group members will draw for assignments.

Draw a chart that looks like this:

	Number of animals	What they eat	Place of protection	Number of animals left after lunch
Grasshopper				
Mouse				
Snake				
Owl				

• Make signs to wear using construction paper and string. Represent each kind of animal with a different color. In large letters, write on your sign the name of the animal that you will portray. Take your sign and your Food Chain Chart to the Field Site when you plan to play Lunch Tag.

 ## Alternate Activity

Write the word or draw a picture of a grasshopper, mouse, snake and owl on strips of paper. Using staples or tape, make the strips into loops that you link into a chain, being careful to add each link in its appropriate place depending on who eats what. Can you come up with other "food chains" with other animals? Do any of your chains link together at some point?

 ## At the Field Site

Picnic
If possible, have everyone pack his or her own lunch for a picnic at the Field Site. Discuss what you are eating. Is it plant or animal? What is the natural source of the food? Discuss what's left after you eat. Can it be recycled, reused, or composted?

Lunch Tag

Remembering your animal's place of protection listed on the Animal Food Chain Chart, find a spot at the Field Site that will represent this place. (Examples: the owl's place could be beside a particular tree; the snake's spot could be near a fence, etc.) Now you are ready to play Lunch Tag.

- Use a whistle or other signal. At the first signal, all animals should position themselves at their place of protection, or "home."

- At the second signal, animals must leave their "homes" and hunt for "lunch." When animals are in danger of being eaten, they may run back to their "homes" Animals are safe when they are touching "home." Any incorrect tagging eliminates the player from the game. (Example: a grasshopper may not tag the owl.) When an animal is tagged, it is "eaten out of the game" and should join the Adventure Leader.

- Signal the end of the game after five minutes.

- Record on the Animal Food Chain Chart the number of animals that were left at the end of the game. Animals that did not hunt for "lunch" died of starvation! No overeating and no chewing allowed!

Leader: If your first try at this game is only hilarious fun with no learning, try it again so that students will understand that they are acting out a food chain. If the game gets too noisy, remind them that they are actually playing the role of an animal, and therefore they should only make the sounds their particular animal would make.

 ## At the Lab

Discussion

How many grasshoppers did one mouse eat? Do you think it was still hungry? Why were the grasshoppers important to the snake? To the owl? Did all of the animals eat lunch? Which animals were alive at the end of Lunch Tag?

What animal is at the top of the food chain you just acted out? What is at the bottom? What would happen to the food chain if all the owls were gone? Or if all the mice were gone?

 ## Alternate Activities

What do you think the animals at the Field Site eat for "lunch?" List five possible food chains using your Field Site inventories.

If you were to invite an animal to your house for a meal, what would you serve it? Select one animal from the Lunch Menu. In the center of a paper plate, draw a picture of that animal and write its name. Around it, draw pictures of different plants/animals eaten by the animal you selected.

Notes

_____

_____

_____

_____

_____

_____

_____

_____

_____

_____

_____

_____

_____

_____

_____

_____

_____

_____

_____

_____

_____

_____

Notes

_____

_____

Leader: Additional terms and concepts can easily be introduced in this Adventure should the interest and aptitude of the students and the time you have warrant it.

Predator-prey relationships: What is a predator? What is prey? Can an animal be both predator and prey? Give examples of each.

Food pyramid: In progressing from the bottom to the top of the food chain, at each level fewer individuals can be supported by the level below it. Therefore, animals lower on the food chain occur in greater numbers than those higher up. As a group, graph the number of leaves required to support the grasshoppers, the number of grasshoppers required to support the mice, and so on up the food chain to the owl at the top. This graphing will result in a triangle known as a food pyramid.

 ## Journal Activity

Plant of the Week: _____

Bug of the Week: _____

Word of the Week: _____

Word Review (fill in the blanks):

role, prey, predator, edible
If the Great-horned Owl eats a snake, the owl is the _____ and the snake is the _____. It is difficult to play the _____ of the snake because you must watch out for the owl while you search for animals that are _____.

sources, determine
When we brought our lunches for a picnic at the Field Site, we tried to _____ the natural _____ of our food.

food pyramid, lower, higher, survival
Animals _____ on the _____ rely on animals _____ on the chain for their _____.

Lunch Menu

MAMMALS

Squirrel: nuts and other tree fruits, buds, bark, birds

Rat: almost anything organic

Dog: meat

Opossum: almost anything organic; eggs are a favorite

Rabbit: plants, tree bark, vegetables, fruit

Domestic Cat: birds, mammals (such as rabbits, rats and mice)

Bat: small flying insects

Human: meat, vegetables, fruit, nuts

BIRDS

House Sparrow: insects, grain, crabgrass seeds, crumbs

European Starling: insects, grain, fruits

American Robin: worms, snails, caterpillars, grasshoppers, small snakes, baby fish, blueberries, cherries, poison ivy berries

Northern Cardinal: caterpillars, grasshoppers, beetles, wild fruit, plant seeds, cultivated grains

Rock Pigeon: seeds

American Kestrel: mice, insects

INVERTEBRATES

Worm: rotting leaves in soil

Sowbug: rotting leaves in soil, tender roots, shoots

Monarch Caterpillar: milkweed leaves

Monarch Butterfly: nectar

Monarch Pupa: does not eat

Ground Beetle: caterpillars

Ants: insects, nectar, bits of garbage

Spider: insects

Sulphur Caterpillar: leaves

Sulphur Butterfly: nectar

Sulphur Pupa: does not eat

Japanese Beetle: flowers, leaves

Weaving a Web Resources

Anthony, Joseph. *In a Nutshell.* Nevada City, CA: Dawn Publications, 1999.

McKinney, Barbara Shaw. *Pass the Energy, Please!* Nevada City, CA: Dawn Publications, 1999.

Pollan, Michael. *The Omnivore's Dilemma: The Secrets Behind What You Eat.* Young readers ed. New York: Dial Books, 2009.

Spilsbury, Louise. *Food Chains and Webs: From Producers to Decomposers.* Chicago: Heinemann, 2004.

Food Web Game: coolclassroom.org/ cool_windows/home.html

Supplies

String or yarn

Paper

Marker

Tape

Weaving a Web

Wild, Wonderful Words

complex   endemic   interweave

All the possible food chains for an animal community form a food web.

Mission:

• To become familiar with the nature of a food web.

 ## At the Field Site

Be a detective and look for evidence of plants and animals being eaten at the field site. Write about or draw what you see. Are there acorn shells, chewed leaves, missing branches or other such signs?

 ## Alternate Activity

Discussion

You have acted out a food chain in Lunch Tag. In a natural community there are many food chains that interweave with one another to form a complex food web.

Preparation

If you haven't already, complete the Alternate Activity in **Lunch** and create five food chains. Using the animals and plants in those food chains, prepare to weave a food web. List the animals, plant materials and other food sources that you feel are necessary. Be sure to include rotting leaves, seeds, berries and some nuts for the squirrel. Using the list you have prepared, make signs for all participants to wear. Pass out the signs.

Tell the students that if the sign they are wearing is an animal name, they are responsible for finding at least one thing the animal eats and remembering it. Give each student a length of string.

Weaving the Web

The Adventure Leader is the Weaver. Have the students sit in a large circle on the floor. The Weaver asks each animal player what it eats and then takes one end of the string the player is holding and gives it to the person who is that player's food. The Weaver will proceed around the circle and weave strings from each animal to the food it eats. It is very important that you hold the strings down on the floor to avoid tripping the Weaver.

Did you weave a good web? If not, have a few people change seats, or ask some animals to select another food from their food list.

This is only a partial food web. Discuss how complicated it would be if the web were completed by connecting each animal to all the foods on its food list. Then consider how the web might be different if a non-native species of plant or animal was introduced that pushed a native species out of the web. Would part of the web start to unravel?

NOTE: If you are working with a single child, tape the signs around the perimeter of a table. Have the child be the weaver and use tape to secure strings between the signs to "weave" the food web.

If there's time, repeat the activity using different colored strands of yarn. Students can note that certain animals can feed on many different things, some animals are the prey for many different organisms and, also, that some plants and/or animals are "picky eaters" — feeding on only one kind of plant. During discussion, the leader can ask students to discuss the pros and cons of eating only one type of thing.

Words to Know

Native species: Species that historically have occurred or evolved in a location.

Non-native species: Species intentionally or accidentally introduced from another location that don't necessarily harm local habitats.

Invasive species: Non-native species that cause economic or environmental harm or harm to human health.

 Journal Activity

Plant of the Week: _____

Bug of the Week: _____

Word of the Week: _____

Word Review (fill in the blanks):

endemic, field site

_____ species are those native to your _____.

Common Denominators Resources

Kalman, Bobbie. *What is a Life Cycle?* New York: Crabtree Pub., 1998.

McKinney, Barbara Shaw. *A Drop Around the World.* Nevada City, CA: Dawn Publications, 1998.

Reilly, Kathleen M. *Explore Life Cycles! 25 Great Projects, Activities, Experiments.* White River Junction, VT: Nomad Press, 2011.

Stewart, Melissa. *Water. National Geographic Kids Readers.* Washington, DC: National Geographic, 2014.

Wick, Walter. *A Drop of Water: A Book of Science and Wonder.* New York: Scholastic, 1997.

Surf Your Watershed, cfpub.epa.gov/surf/locate/index.cfm

Ohio Watershed Network, ohiowatersheds.osu.edu/

Source for butterflies to raise: www.insectlore.com/

How to make a bug jar: planetpals.com/craft_recycle_bug_Jar_kit.html

Common Denominators

Wild, Wonderful Words

basic	evaporated	oxygen	species
carbon dioxide	fuel	pupa	standing water
diversity	larva	pupate	terrarium
droplet	life cycles	shelter	watershed
emerge			

You have learned that there is great diversity in the animal kingdom. Now discover in what ways all animals are the same.

Mission:

To become aware that all animals have the same basic needs of water, food, oxygen, shelter and the ability to produce young.

 **At the Lab**

Discussion

What do you, an earthworm, American Robin and a dog require that are the same?

 At the Field Site

Investigation: All Animals Need Water

After a rain, visit the Field Site. Look for places where you can find standing water. Where can an animal get a drink? (Examples: water collected in a leaf, a puddle on the ground.)

Where can an animal get water if it doesn't rain for a week? (Examples: from food, from dew on the ground in the morning.)

Which animals can leave the Field Site to find water?

Where does the water go after it falls on the Field Site? If it runs into storm drains, where do those lead? Storm-drain runoff sometimes goes directly into local rivers and streams. The area of land that drains into a body of water is called a watershed. Find out which watershed your community is located within by using the websites noted in the Resources section in the sidebar.

It's possible to capture some of the stormwater runoff from a house or building in a rain barrel so that it can be used when conditions are dry again. Consider whether a rain barrel could be used where you live. Sketch a potential rain barrel setup in your journal.

 **At the Lab**

Discussion

All animals need food. Look at the Lunch Menu on page 23.

All animals need oxygen. Where does the oxygen come from?

Did you know that animals could not exist without the oxygen produced by plants? Other ways in which animals depend on plants are discussed in the **Weeds and Seeds** Adventure.

All animals need shelter. Refer to your Field Site inventory. Where does each of the animals live? Next time you visit the Field Site, look for as many animal homes as you can find. How is each home suited to its tenant? Is it near food? Does the home provide protection for the animal and its young?

Pick one animal from your Field Site inventory and draw a picture of its home in your journal. Write a description of the home. Visit the library for reference books or search the internet for information you can use to find this information.

Leader: Plants take in carbon dioxide and water. With energy from the sun, these are turned into food and oxygen is given off. Animals breathe oxygen. In the animal's body, oxygen is used to burn fuel (food). This process gives the animal energy. Carbon dioxide is released.

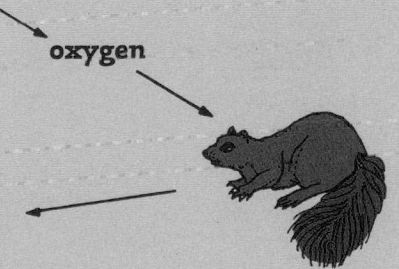

 At the Field Site

Life Cycles

All animal species need to be able to produce young. Observe as much as you can of the life cycles of the tenants at the Field Site. If long-term observation is not possible, make observations for one season or for part of the life cycle. Watch how and if the parents care for the young.

Examples:
- A robin lays eggs in a nest. The parents keep the eggs warm until the babies hatch. The babies stay in the nest, grow feathers and leave when they can fly.
- A butterfly lays eggs and then flies away. Each egg hatches into a larva, or caterpillar. A caterpillar becomes a pupa, which hatches into a butterfly.
- A mosquito lays eggs in standing, or stagnant, water. Each egg hatches into a larva. A larva becomes a pupa, which hatches into an adult mosquito.

Leader: An excellent way to bring the concept of a life cycle to life is to watch a butterfly move through its phases of development. Consider ordering a butterfly kit (see the Resources section of this guide for sources) and setting it up at the Lab for students to observe.

Alternately, if you find a larva at your Field Site, you might also consider bringing it back to the Lab for observation.

Observing a larva at the Lab:

1. Bring to the classroom the section of the plant containing the leaf that the larva is eating.
2. Put the stem of the section in a container of water. You may wish to do this project in a terrarium.
3. Change plant material often enough to keep the larva supplied with fresh food. Be sure to supply the same kind of plant material.
4. Under these simple conditions, the larva will pupate and often emerge as an adult insect.
5. After a short period of observation, release the adult insect in the same area where you found the larva.

 Alternate Activities

Life Cycle

Draw the life cycle — or at least one stage in the life cycle — of one tenant of the Field Site. Keep this drawing in your journal.

What other cycles are at work at your Field Site? A rainy or cloudy day is a great time to think about the water cycle. Chart the cycle of a drop of rain that falls on the Field Site until it returns to the clouds.

Example:

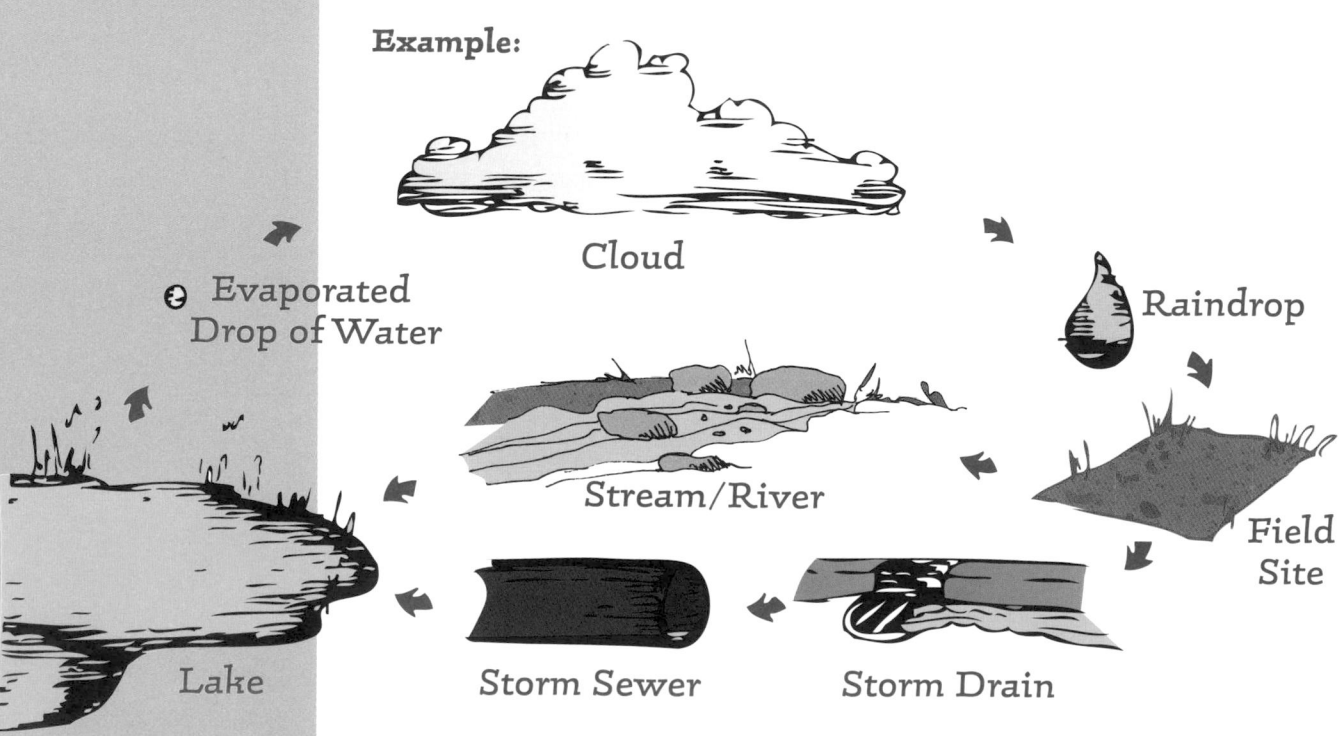

Cloud

Evaporated Drop of Water

Raindrop

Stream/River

Field Site

Lake

Storm Sewer

Storm Drain

 **Journal Activity**

Plant of the Week: _____

Bug of the Week: _____

Word of the Week: _____

Word Review (fill in the blanks):

basic, oxygen, species
All _____ of animals have the same _____ needs: shelter, protection, food, _____ and the ability to produce young.

evaporated, standing water, organisms, stagnant
A puddle is _____ before it has _____. _____ water can become very smelly because _____ grow in it, decompose and are trapped there.

research, larva, emerge, pupates
If we collect a _____, we must do some _____ to find out how to care for it. When the insect _____, it will no longer need nourishment and after some time will _____ as an adult.

Weeds and Seeds Resources

Anthony, Joseph P. *The Dandelion Seed.* Nevada City, CA: Dawn Publications, 1997.

Hiebert, Helen. *Papermaking with Plants: Creative Recipes and Projects Using Herbs, Flowers, Grasses, and Leaves.* Pownal, VT: Storey Books, 1998.

Himmelman, John. *A Dandelion's Life.* New York: Children's Press, 1998.

Newcomb, Lawrence. *Newcomb's Wildflower Guide.* Reprint ed. Boston: Little, Brown and Company, 1989.

Kids Gardening.org: www.kidsgardening.org

The Science of Spring: Plant, Grow, Learn! seeds.sciencenetlinks.com

Seed Saving with Children: www. gardeningknowhow.com/special/children/ seed-saving-with-children.htm

Grow a garden for birds: http://www. audubon.org/plantsforbirds

Supplies

Egg carton

Poster board

Markers

Glue

Weeds and Seeds

Wild, Wonderful Words

aerate	efficient	parachute	survival
airborne	erosion	quadrant	transpiration
buffers	habitat	specimens	urban
classified	jeopardize	stress	vast
composite	organisms		

Plants are living organisms. The life cycle of flowering plants is seed-plant-flower-fruit-seed. Plants cannot move from place to place, yet plants appear in new areas.

Missions:
- To become aware of the life cycle of plants.
- To become aware of the large numbers of seeds plants produce.
- To discover how fruits and seeds travel.
- To recognize the importance of plants.

 At the Field Site

Leader: Tell students that removing specimens from park areas and private property is generally prohibited. Activities in this Adventure are not in conflict with these rules if you have permission to use the Field Site for a learning experience. Limited collecting of a few specimens can be a useful teaching tool, but remind students that photographs and drawings are generally the most respectful way to study living things.

Flowers

Look for flowers on the plants at the Field Site during all four seasons. (Don't forget that trees are plants.) First, stop to enjoy their beauty. Do all the plants at the Field Site have flowers? Look carefully!

Find a plant that is blooming. Are there many flowers on the plant? Pick a flower and pull it apart. Is it made up of many little flowers?

A single dandelion bloom is not one flower, but many. Each yellow ray of a single bloom is actually one flower that will produce a seed. Other examples of this type of flower head are goldenrod, sunflower and black-eyed Susan. On some plants, the flowers are so small that you need a magnifying glass to see them. (Examples: grasses, lamb's quarter, ragweed, plantain.) Compare these flowers with a rose you may have seen. Each rose is one flower.

Fruits

Fruits are produced by flowers. Look for fruits. You will find them after the flowers have bloomed. The fruit of the dandelion hangs below the white fuzzy parachute that forms after the bloom. The fruit of the milkweed plant is an easily identified pod. Sometimes you find flowers and fruits on a plant at the same time. (Examples: evening primrose, peppergrass.) What do the fruits you found at the Field Site look like? Have you ever seen the fruit of a rose? What is the fruit of an apple tree?

Seeds

All fruits contain one or more seeds. The seed of the dandelion is contained in the fruit hanging below the white fuzzy parachute. The airborne objects blowing away from the milkweed fruit (pod) are seeds. But similar-looking objects blowing away from aster, goldenrod and fleabane flowers are actually fruits. Birds eat the seeds, usually after the fruits split apart. Sometimes birds eat entire fruits, such as mulberries, cherries and blackberries, seeds and all. Where are the seeds of an apple tree? Look for what you think are seeds. Think about whether you eat any seeds in your diet. What is a nut? An acorn is the fruit of an oak tree. It is called a nut. A nut is a single seeded fruit.

Leader: The distinction between fruit and seed can be confusing. Emphasize the seed-plant-flower-fruit-seed life cycle. Whether airborne objects are fruits or seeds is not critical at this level of learning.

Weed-Fruit and Weed-Seed Scavenger Hunt

Collect as many kinds of fruits and seeds as you can find and place them in an egg carton or ice cube tray. Collect two of each kind.

 ## At the Lab

Discussion

Arrival

How did the fruits and seeds arrive at the Field Site? (Examples: by wind, water, animal.) Try to figure out the different methods of travel for the fruits and seeds you collected. (Examples: beggar-ticks and burdock stuck on your clothing; dandelion and milkweed blown by the wind; mulberry seed deposited in the droppings of a bird flying over the Field Site.) Which fruits and seeds do you think are good travelers?

Divide the fruits and seeds that were collected into two groups. In the first group, put all those fruits and seeds that you think are blown by the wind. In the second, put all those that you think animals might carry in some way. Mount each group on a large poster board or keep in your journal. (You may want to press the seeds between paper using books or a plant press before you do so.) Use only one of each kind of seed. Save the other for the "Flying Contest" at the Field Site.

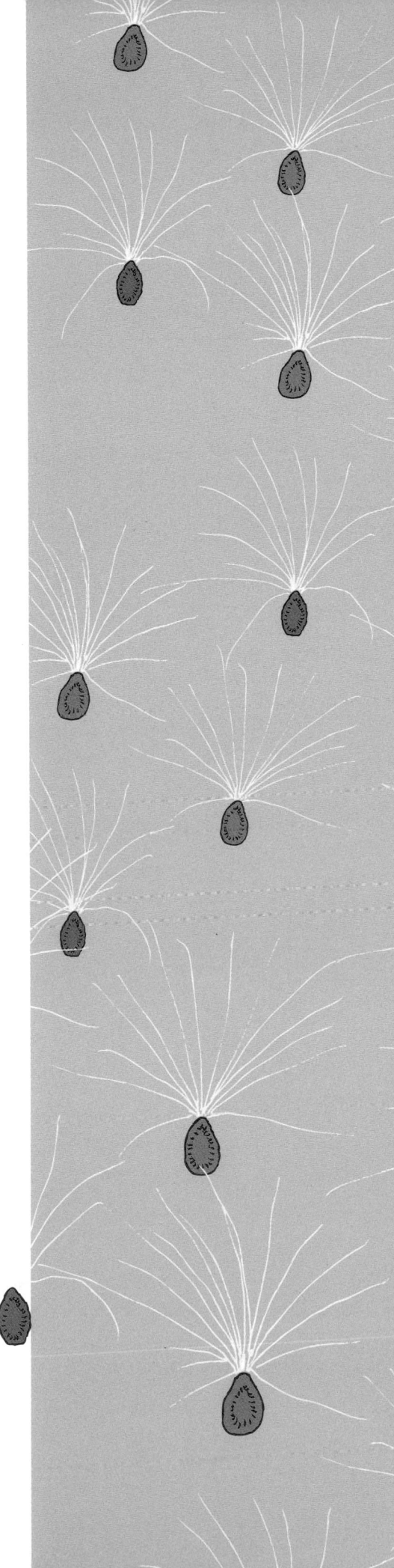

Continue to do this activity all year, adding different seeds to the collection. Record the date each seed was gathered. Check your clothing each time you leave the Field Site to see if you are a seed carrier.

Survival

How do flowers help urban plants survive? Many urban plants belong to the composite family. Composites are plants that produce many blooms. Each bloom is made up of many tiny flowers. Remember the dandelion? One composite plant produces thousands of flowers, each of which becomes a fruit that contains the seed.

 ## At the Field Site

Flying Contest

On a windy day, take the extra fruits and seeds to the Field Site. From as high a spot as possible, release them one at a time. Watch them fly. If possible, mark where the fruits and seeds fall to earth. Pace off the distances. What fruit or seed wins the Flying Contest? Did all the fruits and seeds you had classified as "wind-blown" fly well? Did the fruits and seeds that were "animal carried" land closer to where they were released? What general conclusions can you draw?

 ## At the Lab

Long-Term Observation

Plant a sunflower or other seed. Count the days until it germinates. Measure the seedling each day and record its growth in your journal. Transplant the seedling into a larger pot or, if the season is right, into an outdoor garden. Continue to track its growth.

 ## Alternate Activities

Seed Sort

Put a selection of different seeds in an egg carton or empty ice cube tray.

Look at the seeds under a magnifying glass. Are they fuzzy? Spiny? Smooth? What color are they? Do they make a distinct sound when you drop them?

Make a drawing of each seed and record your observations about it in your journal.

Weed Definition

Discuss with the group what the term "weed" means to you. Look up the word in the dictionary. Write a group definition for "weed." Copy it into your journal. Add drawings of some of the weeds you've seen.

Discuss what urban plants do for you (remember, trees are plants). (Examples: prevent erosion, produce oxygen, provide shade, cool the air in the summer through transpiration, filter the impurities out of the air, act as sound buffers, serve as homes for animals, provide food for animals, aerate the soil with their roots.) Do you think the plants that live in the city should be called weeds? Should the name of this Adventure be "Weeds and Seeds"?

 Journal Activity

Plant of the Week: _____

Bug of the Week: _____

Word of the Week: _____

Word Review (fill in the blanks):

urban, stress, habitat

The _____ environment is a good _____ for city-plant species because their survival depends on _____.

composite, survival, airborne

The _____ of the dandelion in the city is assured because each plant has _____ blooms that produce many, many seeds. The seeds become _____ and "parachute" to new locations.

Soil Appreciation Day

Himmelman, John. *An Earthworm's Life.* New York: Children's Press, 2001.

Loewen, Nancy. *Garden Wigglers: Earthworms in Your Backyard.* Minneapolis: Picture Window Books, 2006.

Rosinsky, Natalie M. Dirt: *The Scoop on Soil.* Minneapolis: Picture Window Books, 2002.

Schuh, Mari. *Soil Basics.* Mankato, MN: Capstone Press, 2012.

Silverstein, Alvin. *Life in a Bucket of Soil.* Minneola, NY: Dover Publications, 2000.

Do virtual composting: www.pbslearningmedia.org/resource/ess05.sci.ess.earthsys.compost/compost-office/

Find your Cooperative Extension System office: www.csrees.usda.gov/Extension/

Do the Rot Thing: www.cvswmd.org/uploads/6/1/2/6/6126179/do_the_rot_thing_cvswmd1.pdf

The Dirt on Soil: school.discoveryeducation.com/schooladventures/soil/name_soil.html

Great Lakes Worm Watch: greatlakeswormwatch.org

Soil Appreciation Day

Wild, Wonderful Words

nourish	inorganic	humus	formation
ingredient	particles	vermiculture	organic

Your parents may not like the soil you bring home on your face, hands and shoes, but soil at the Field Site is very important.

Missions:
- To begin to understand what soil really is.
- To begin to understand the importance of soil.
- To learn where soil comes from and where it goes.

 ## At the Field Site

Leader: At the end of this Adventure is a sample Soil Research Sheet. Reproduce it for each member of your group. Feel free to add questions. Fold each sheet in half.

Soil Research

You will be given a Soil Research Sheet (located on page 37) with questions on it. Keep it folded.

Find a spot where you can sit on the ground, 10 feet away from the next person. At the signal, open the folded paper, read the questions, think about the soil underneath you, and write the answers to the questions. Observe carefully.

 ## At the Lab

Discussion
Discuss the answers on the Soil Research Sheet.

Consider this statement: "In a natural community, plants supply food for animals." How does this statement relate to the question "What does soil do for you?" Would there be plants for plant-eaters to eat if there were no soil to nourish and support plants? What would the meat-eaters eat if there were no plant-eaters? What would happen to the food chain?

Read all answers to Part Three on the Soil Research Sheet. Using these, write a definition of soil. Put your Soil Research Sheet and definition of soil in your journal.

Leader: After you have completed your definition of soil, read the following: Soil is composed of both organic and inorganic material. The organic material, called humus, consists of decomposed plants and animals. It is a small part of the soil, but the most important part. The inorganic material consists of small bits of concrete, rock, stone, sand or brick that have been worn away by the effects of climate. This wearing is caused by such things as freezing and thawing, sun, rain and wind.

 # At the Field Site

The Search

What evidence is there at the Field Site that tells you that soil formation is going on?

Find organic material that can decompose to become humus. (Examples: dead animal or plant, decaying piece of wood.) Find decomposers at work. (Examples: worm, sowbug, centipede, millipede.) Decomposers turn dead organic material into humus.

Find examples of the sources of the inorganic material in the soil, such as a worn step, a crumbling brick or concrete block, candy wrapper, chip bag, bits of pavement broken off by the action of plant growth.

Discussion

Where did the soil at the Field Site come from? (Examples: formed at the Field Site, blown to the Field Site, brought by rainwater, brought by a dump truck.)

Will soil leave the Field Site? How? (Examples: on your shoes, erosion by wind or water runoff, birds taking dust baths.)

Did you find any earthworms during your soil research? If you live in a part of North America that was covered by a glacier during the Ice Age, any earthworms you find in the soil are invasive non-native species that were brought here by early Europeans. During the Ice Age, the intense cold and upper soil layer removal by the glaciers killed off the native earthworms. The non-native earthworms are changing the soil in ways that disturb native ecosystems that established after the glaciers retreated. Native earthworms live in the unglaciated portion of North America. However, earthworms from Asia have become established in areas along the East Coast and are starting to slowly work their way west.

 # Alternate Activity

Using the internet, your local library or state Cooperative Extension office, learn about composting and vermiculture (composting with worms). See the **Resources** section of this Adventure for more information.

Journal Activity

Plant of the Week: _____

Bug of the Week: _____

Word of the Week: _____

Word Review (fill in the blanks):

organic, particles, inorganic

Soil is composed of _____, both _____ and
_____.

organic, humus, ingredient

When _____ material, either plant or animal, is allowed
to decompose, it will form _____, which is a rich
_____ of soil.

nourishment, water, sun

Plants receive _____ and energy from the soil,
_____ and the _____.

Soil Research Sheet

Part I:

Is the soil loosely packed? ☐ Yes ☐ No ☐ Other: _____

Is it like the clay that artists work with? ☐ Yes ☐ No

Take a piece of soil and rub it between your fingers. What does it feel like? _____

Is the soil damp or dry? _____

Are the particles all the same size? _____

What kinds of materials do you think are in the soil? _____

_____

Are some of them human-made? ☐ Yes ☐ No ☐ I don't know.

What are they? _____

With a stick, dig down deeper into the soil. What is happening in the soil?

_____

Are things moving in the soil? _____ What are they? _____

Are things growing in the soil? ☐ Yes ☐ No Name them:. _____

Can you tell whether plants would grow well or poorly in the area where you are sitting?

☐ Yes ☐ No Why? _____

Smell the soil. What does it smell like? Does it smell good or bad? _____

What five words would help you describe your soil sample?

_____ , _____ , _____ , _____ , _____

Part II:

What does soil do for you? _____

Part III:
What is soil? _____

_____

Signs of Seasons Resources

Bernard, Robin. *A Tree for All Seasons*. Washington: National Geographic Society, 2001.

Branley, Franklin M. *Sunshine Makes the Seasons*. New York: HarperCollins, 2005.

Eckart, Edana. *Watching the Seasons*. New York: Children's Press, 2004.

Magney, Troy, et al. 2013. Keeping a (Digital) Eye on Nature's Clock: Students Use Digital Cameras to Monitor Plant Phenology. *Science Teacher* 80 (1): 37-43.

Neil, Kaesha. 2009. Flowering Phenology: An Activity to Introduce Human & Environmental Effects on Plant Reproduction. *American Biology Teacher* 71 (5): 300-304.

USA National Phenology Network: usanpn.org

Project BudBurst (citizen science project): www.budburst.org

eBird (record your bird sightings): ebird.org/content/ebird/

Community Collaborative Rain, Hail and Snow Network: www.cocorahs.org/

FrogWatch USA (report data on frogs in your community): www.aza.org/frogwatch

Journey North (track seasonal change): http://www.learner.org/jnorth/

Signs of Seasons

Wild, Wonderful Words

entry	renew	valid
progression	significant	phenology

There is an orderly progression of seasonal change in the plant and animal kingdom that is repeated year after year.

Mission:
- To observe evidence of seasonal change.

 ## At the Field Site

Now

What season is it now? What signs of the season do you see, hear, smell or feel?

"I Spy"

If you're working in a group, divide into teams. Individuals or teams should take along a page from their journal or other paper with "I Spy" written across the top. List any evidence you see of seasonal change. (Examples: dried stalks from last fall, brown leaves on the ground, an old bird's nest, a tiny tree seedling growing between the asphalt and the curb.) Share your results.

Tenant's Diary

Choose one plant or animal from the Field Site inventory. (Remember that trees are large plants.) In your journal, write weekly observations for one year, or as long a time as possible, about your plant or animal. Be sure to date each entry. This will be your Tenant's Diary. Add drawings to the Tenant's Diary that show significant changes. If possible, take photographs occasionally and mount them in the diary.

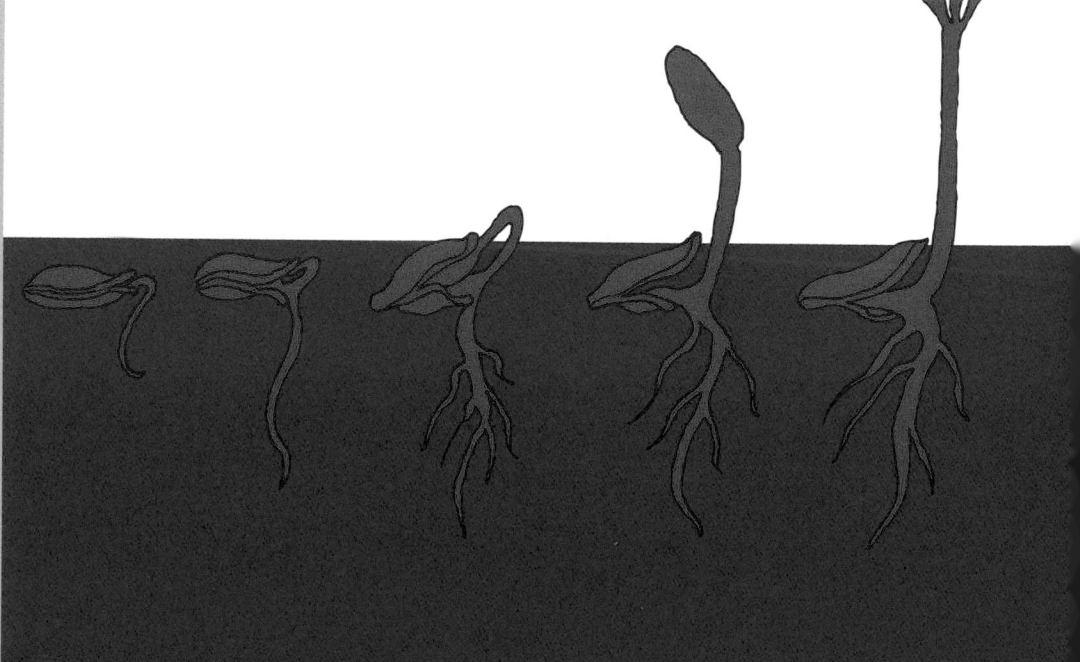

Alternate Activities

Rainy Day "I Spy"
Put on your boots and coat/rain poncho or grab an umbrella. You can do "I Spy" in the rain!

Spot Seasonal Change
Phenology is the study of how the lives of plants and animals are connected to climate and seasonal changes. Anyone can participate in phenology by making observations of living organisms over time. Students can try this by taking a photo or making a drawing of the same spot at least once during all four seasons, or more frequently over a shorter time frame. As new photos are added, compare them and point out what is different.

Journal Activity

Plant of the Week: _____

Bug of the Week: _____

Word of the Week: _____

Word Review (fill in the blanks):

significant, progression
We expect the orderly _____ of the seasons.
If we had snowstorms every July for several years, we would find such a change in our climate _____.

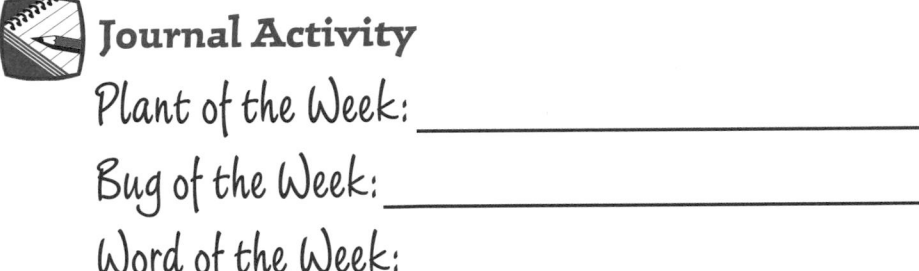

The ABCs of Change Resources

Branley, Franklin M. *The Moon Seems to Change*. New York: HarperCollins, 1987.

Dorros, Arthur. *Feel the Wind*. New York: HarperCollins, 2000.

Koontz, Robin. *Erosion: Changing Earth's Surface.* Minneapolis: Picture Window Books, 2007.

Mason, Adrienne. *Change It! Solids, Liquids, Gases and You*. Toronto: Kids Can Press, 2006.

Brain Pop Spotlight: Forces of Nature: www.brainpop.com/spotlight/forcesofnature/

The ABCs of Change

Wild, Wonderful Words

constantly   eroding   nouns   verbs

Everything is constantly changing. Concrete is slowly eroding. Cloud patterns are continually changing. You are growing up!

Missions:
- To become aware that everything is constantly changing.
- To use nouns and verbs in sentences.

 ## At the Lab

The Alphabet
Discuss the difference between nouns and verbs. Each student should write across the top of a big piece of paper "Noun Alphabet Game." Letter the alphabet down the left-hand side. Turn the paper over and write "Verb Alphabet Game" across the top, and letter down the side.

 ## At the Field Site

Observation
Look for changes that are taking place.

Noun Alphabet Game
After each letter, or after as many as possible, write a simple sentence about a change you see at the Field Site that uses a noun starting with that letter. (Examples: An ant is carrying a grain of sand. A brick is crumbling. A cloud is moving.) Underline the letter of the alphabet in each noun.

Verb Alphabet Game

On the other side of the paper, write sentences about changes you see using as many verbs as you can that start with the letters of the alphabet. (Examples: The boys arrive to pick up litter. The sun bakes the dirt. The wind cools the student.) Underline the letter of the alphabet in the verb.

 ## At the Lab

Share your sentences from the Noun Alphabet Game. If working with a group, have each child tally up the number of sentences with nouns used correctly. Who had the most?

Do the same for the Verb Alphabet Game. Keep your paper in your journal.

Leader: This activity can be done indoors on a rainy day. Use a photo of your Field Site or look at a picture from a natural area for reference.

 ## Journal Activity

Plant of the Week: _____

Bug of the Week: _____

Word of the Week: _____

Word Review (fill in the blanks):

verbs, change
_____ show action. _____ is an action that is constantly at work.

Time Capsule Resources

Cherry, Lynne. *A River Ran Wild: An Environmental History.* San Diego: Harcourt Brace Jovanovich, 1992.

Lehman, Barbara. *The Secret Box.* Boston: Houghton Mifflin Books for Children, 2011.

Pryor, Bonnie. *The House on Maple Street.* New York: HarperCollins, 1992.

Teaching with Primary Sources from the Library of Congress: www.loc.gov/teachers/classroommaterials/

Time Capsule

Wild, Wonderful Words

capsule   drawing conclusions   stump
designate   exhibiting

Life is constantly changing. The Field Site has not always looked the way it does today. We will investigate what happens to things over time.

Missions:
- To become aware of long-term changes in nature caused by human beings.
- To practice drawing conclusions from observations.
- To practice speculating about the future through evidence from the past and present.

 ## At the Field Site

Picturing the Present
Draw a picture of a scene from your Field Site as it looks today in your journal.

Picturing the Future
Draw a picture of the same scene as it might look 10 years from now. What changes have you incorporated into your drawing?

 ## At the Lab

Discussion
Look at your drawing of the Field Site as it is today. What, if anything, is located where it is as a result of human activity? Be sure to consider whether the plants you drew might be non-native species that people brought from other parts of the world (some examples of these would be Japanese knotweed, garlic mustard or tree of heaven).

Talk about all the factors that could affect the Field Site in the next 10 years. Will trees grow bigger? If so, how will this affect the plants near them? "Ecological succession" is a term scientists use to talk about the ways natural communities change over time. Discuss ways in which a major change like a fire or flood would change the Field Site and how this type of sweeping change could be both negative and positive.

Leader: Investigate whether historical photos of your community are available or an old photograph of the field site (e.g., backyard). Display these as additional examples of change (in this case, human-caused) over time.

 # Alternate Activities

A Backward Look

What do you think the Field Site looked like when Native Americans lived here? When the settlers arrived? When it first became part of a small town?

Art Gallery

Create a picture that tells something about one period you have imagined in the life history of the Field Site. Make an Art Gallery at the Lab.

100 Years in the Future

Write a short story about what you think will have changed at the Field Site one hundred years from now. What will cause these changes?

 # Journal Activity

Plant of the Week: _____

Bug of the Week: _____

Word of the Week: _____

Word Review (fill in the blanks):

capsule, designate

In a time _____ you _____ items that have meaning for the time period in which you live.

43

Create Change Resources

Burton, Virginia Lee. *The Little House.* 70th Anniversary ed. Boston: Houghton Mifflin, 2012.

Earthworks Group. *The New 50 Simple Things Kids Can Do to Save the Earth.* Kansas City: Andrews McMeel, 2009.

Sirett, Dawn, et al. *Love Your World: How to Take Care of the Plants, the Animals, and the Planet.* New York: DK Publishing, 2009.

Vogel, Carole Garbuny. *Human Impact.* New York: F. Watts, 2003.

Walsh, Melanie. *10 Things I Can Do to Help My World.* Reprint ed. Cambridge, MA: Candlewick Press, 2012.

The Great Lake Erie Boat Float: www.lakeerieboatfloat.org

Plastic Pollution: www.5gyres.org

Create Change

Wild, Wonderful Words

chain of events   control   gullies   periodic

conclusive   experimentation   mini-park   square meter

You can cause changes in nature.

Missions:

- To become more aware of how human action causes change.
- To experience the use of a "control" in experimentation.
- To practice recording changes through periodic observations.
- To practice hypothesizing on the basis of observations of change.

 **At the Lab**

Discussion

Discuss how human actions cause changes in nature.

If you're working in a group, divide into teams. Decide on one change that you can create at the Field Site that will result in changes in the natural community. (Examples: remove vegetation from an area of ground to create a bare spot of earth, on a slope if possible; put a board over a section of ground; constantly water a dry section; add soil and plant grass seed in a bare area. The last three changes need to be made during the growing season to produce evidence of change.)

 At the Field Site

Prepare for the Change

Draw pictures of and take detailed notes on the present condition of the area at the Field Site that you are about to change. Do the same for an area right next to it that will be your "control" area. Be sure to check and record the condition of the soil and information about the small animals in the soil.

Make the Change

Carry out your change.

Observe the Area

Make weekly observations for at least four weeks. Take careful notes on what is happening in the "change" area and in the "control" area.

Possible Observations:

- If you have created a bare spot of earth, check for evidence of erosion. Here are a few suggested activities:
  - Before a rain, drive a flat stick into the middle of the bare spot and one into the middle of the "control" area. As soon as possible after the rain, compare the dirt that was splashed onto each stick.
  - Put a square of felt on the ground. After a rainstorm, see if it has moved.
  - Look for channels in the soil that demonstrate erosion.
  - Count the number of exposed pebbles before and after a rainstorm and determine if that number has changed.
- Feel the soil. Is it damp or dry? Warm to the touch or cold?
- Are there more insects or fewer?
- If you removed plants from the soil, has anything started sprouting in their place?

Your chart might look like this:

First Week	Control Area	Change Area
Ground	drier lighter harder	damper darker softer
Animals	occasional ant	sowbugs centipedes millipedes worms
Plants	plant growing well	plants turning yellow

 At the Lab

Discussion

Report on what you observed after your observation period is complete. Discuss what has happened to the plant life, animal life and soil in each change. Discuss anything else that might have resulted from the change. Did the change you made at the Field Site cause one change in nature or many changes? Discuss this question thoroughly.

What changes may be caused by the continued use of the Field Site by your group? (Example: paths.)

Chain-of-Events Chart

Each group prepares a chart that describes what happened during the weekly observations. Compare the data from the "control" area and the "change" area. Connect the chain of events with arrows.

Example:
Made a ➡ spot of earth on a slope. ➡ The ground dried out and was warmer. ➡ The worms and sowbugs disappeared. ➡ Soil was packed down. ➡ Soil splashed onto a flat stick during a rain. ➡ Erosion gullies formed in the bare earth.

Photographs or drawings could record this as well. Mount them on a sheet of poster board and connect with arrows.

Alternate Activity

What If?

Tell a story about what would happen to the natural community at the Field Site if a three-story apartment building were built next door, if a house were built on the Field Site, or if the Field Site were turned into a parking lot.

What would you like to happen to the Field Site? Is there litter you wish were not there? Would the Field Site make a good mini-park? Would you like to plant a small garden on it? Would you like to leave it alone and let nature take care of it?

Journal Activity

Plant of the Week: _____

Bug of the Week: _____

Word of the Week: _____

Word Review (fill in the blanks):

observations, control, periodic
In our Journals we made _____ _____ of the area we changed and the one that served as our _____.

Launch into Learning

Wild, Wonderful Words

hazard	interview	mimics	social structure
stimulating	strides	tale	translate

The Field Site can be used to teach many subjects in an exciting way.

Mission:
• There are lessons in every aspect of nature. Teach others what you've learned about the natural world.

 **At the Lab**

Discussion
Divide into small groups or work individually and select a subject. Plan an adventure at the Field Site that will be a unit in that subject. The following are examples in the different subjects:

Examples of Activities: Language Arts
• Interview a tree, a flower, a bird, an ant or any other living thing. Use your imagination. Write up your interview as a front-page story in a newspaper.
• Select a Field Site tenant. Write a story or poem about it.
• Write a poem using as many "Words of the Week" as possible.

Examples of Activities: Math – Measuring
• Measure one square meter of ground. Inventory the animals and plants you find in one-quarter of the square meter.
• In your journal, draw a plan for a 2-by-2-meter garden that is to scale. What do you want to plant in the rows? Create a budget for your garden (cost of plants or seeds). Find out the grocery store prices for the vegetables in your plan. How many of each kind of vegetable will you need to grow to make your garden profitable?
• Mark off 10 meters on the ground and place a stick at each end. Figure out how you can use your legs to measure one meter by traveling this distance in 10 strides, hops or jumps. Then estimate how many meters wide the Field Site is. Estimate how many meters deep the Field Site is. If you can, check your estimates with a metric tape measure. Estimate and record in your journal the length of the classroom, your home, your bedroom and a car.

Examples of Activities: Music & Dance
• Listen for an animal sound. Translate this sound into a tune. Write words for the tune.
• Form a rhythm band and play the beat of the animal sounds with sticks.
  - Create a dance that mimics the animal's movements.

Launch into Learning Resources

Feinstein, Julie. *Field Guide to Urban Wildlife: Common Animals of Cities and Suburbs: How They Adapt and Thrive.* Mechanicsburg, PA: Stackpole Books, 2011.

Landry, Sarah B. *Peterson First Guide to Urban Wildlife.* Boston: Houghton Mifflin, 1998.

Tredici, Peter Del. *Wild Urban Plants of the Northeast: a Field Guide.* Ithaca: Cornell University Press, 2010.

How to Garden for Wildlife: www.nwf.org/Home/How-to-Help/Garden-for-Wildlife.aspx

How to Make Clay from Indigenous Soil: www.wikihow.com/Make-Clay-from-Indigenous-Soil

Seven Animal Sounds You May Hear in Your Backyard: www.huffingtonpost.com/2013/03/23/animal-sounds-in-backyard_n_2934973.html

Supplies

Meter stick

Examples of Activities: Art

- If you have the correct soil, make clay pots. (To test for this, dig a handful of soil, moisten it and then squeeze it tightly. Open your hand. If the soil falls apart readily, it contains little clay. If it holds together even when you poke it, it's probably mostly clay and will hold its shape when dry.)
- Press wildflowers and use them to decorate notepaper.
- Make leaf or bark rubbings.

Example of Activity: Science

- Find an ant hill. Observe the ants as they enter and leave the hill. What do they do when they leave the hill? Compare their sizes to the sizes of the things they carry.

Example of Activity: Health — Clean up

- Search the Field Site for anything that would be a health hazard. (Examples: broken glass, open can, rusty nail, poison ivy, nightshade berry.) Count what you find and graph it. Discuss the hazards of each one. Discard or recycle items as appropriate.

Journal Activity

Plant of the Week: _____

Bug of the Week: _____

Word of the Week: _____

Word Review (fill in the blanks):

hazard, tale, interview

Broken glass at the field site can be a _____.

What _____ did the flower tell you when you conducted your _____ with it?

48

Tour Guide

Wild, Wonderful Words

browse	evaluation	occasion	reinforces
challenging	manned	precautions	series

Teaching someone else what you have learned reinforces your own learning. At the same time, you are able to share with others the gifts of knowledge that you have received.

Missions:
- To learn by teaching.
- To share knowledge with others.

Develop a simple nature trail at the Field Site and related projects at the Lab that show what you learned on your *Nature in the City* Adventures. Plan a self-guided tour of the nature trail for visitors and prepare displays and demonstrations at the Lab.

Preparation

 ## At the Lab

Goals
Decide why you want to hold your tour and what you want it to accomplish. Write down your objectives and your overall goal.

Nature Trail

Discuss what you have learned about the Field Site. Decide what you think would interest someone not familiar with your site and what things he or she should know (such as the Field Site Code of Conduct). After careful consideration and/or discussion, make a list of what should be included on the nature trail at the Field Site.

Plan the self-guided tour of your Field Site. Make signs pointing out interesting features and/or information and a trail brochure.

Lab Displays and Demonstrations

Decide what exhibits should be set up at the Lab for this Adventure. List them. (Examples: maps, connecting game from **Weaving a Web**, art gallery, creative cartoon, newspaper interview and some Field Site journal pages.) Create any posters you may need.

Plan a performance that highlights what you've learned in some way. This may be the animal sound rhythm you played in the **Launch Into Learning** Adventure or a puppet show using paper bag puppets or another kind of puppet you make yourself.

Tour Guide Resources

Cousins, Lucy. *Maisy's Nature Trail.* London: Walker Books, 2008.

Florian, Douglas. *Nature Walk.* New York: Greenwillow Books, 1989.

Silver, Donald. *One Small Square: Backyard.* New York: McGraw Hill, 1997.

Making Tracks – Trail Guides: makingtrackschallenge.com/

Community Walk: Mapping Made Easy: www.communitywalk.com/

Here is an example of a Communitiy Walk that was created for finding the Moses Cleaveland Trees in the Cleveland area: www.communitywalk.com/map/index/1735566

Invitations

Think up an interesting name for the occasion. Create invitations for family, neighbors and/or friends. (This event also could be used for a parents open house.) Invite them for a two-part event: a field tour outdoors and displays and demonstrations indoors.

Part One: Field Tour

 ## At the Lab

Discussion

Using the two maps posted in your Lab that you created during the **Mapping the Territory** Adventure, explain briefly the route you will take to the Field Site and point out what you've marked on both maps. Discuss the precautions it is necessary to take at these places. Discuss the Field Site Code of Conduct.

 ## At the Field Site

Nature Trail Walk

Hand out copies of the brochure you created and help anyone touring the Field Site.

Part Two: Lab Displays and Demonstrations

 ## At the Lab

Browsing Time

Allow ample time for guests to browse through the exhibits. Be ready to answer questions at each exhibit.

The Performance

Perform your animal-inspired rhythmic pattern from **Launch Into Learning** or your puppet show. Explain which animal is the basis for your performance. Tell your audience all you have learned about that animal.

Evaluation

 At the Lab

Review your objectives for **Tour Guide.** Determine whether you met your overall goal. Did any good things happen that were not included in your objectives? List these. Would you make any changes if you were to repeat **Tour Guide**? List these.

 Journal Activity

Plant of the Week: _____

Bug of the Week: _____

Word of the Week: _____

Word Review (fill in the blanks):

reinforces, challenging, evaluation

Teaching someone else what you have learned _____ your own learning.

Sometimes you can learn the most by _____ yourself to understand a difficult concept.

Send your guests a questionnaire about your event to receive an _____.

Nature in the City Scavenger Hunts

An Introduction

The original *Nature in the City* Adventure Guide featured cards printed with illustrations of an urban Field Site in each of the four seasons, created by artist Lauretta Jones. Each card was perforated so that it could be separated into four sections, with questions on the reverse side about what was pictured.

In the spirit of the original cards, we are pleased to reprint Jones' illustrations on the following pages with an accompanying scavenger hunt-themed activity. Students should examine each lettered quadrant and then look for the plants and/or animals indicated. The activity includes questions for students to think about and discuss.

As students embark on this activity, encourage them to take their time and use their observation skills. Help them appreciate how observations may answer some questions, but create others.

You can use these scavenger hunts as adjuncts to other activities in this guide or reserve them for days when Field Site visits aren't possible.

Encourage students to create their own scavenger hunts, perhaps based on what they see at their own Field Site.

Spring Scavenger Hunt

A Find these animals: squirrel, rat, cat

How are these animals alike? How are they different?

Where has the squirrel built its nest?

What do rats eat? Why is the rat considered a pest?

What does the cat eat? Cats are not a natural part of this scene. Why is it important that we take care of our pets?

All of the animals in the picture are mammals. What makes mammals unique from other animals? Can you name other mammals that live in a city?

B Find these birds: American Robin, House Sparrow, American Kestrel

The return of the American Robin is considered a sign of spring. Where have these birds been? What do they eat? What do robins use to build their nests? Do you know what an American Robin's song sounds like?

What is the House Sparrow doing? What do House Sparrows use to build their nests? Do you know what a House Sparrow's song sounds like?

The American Kestrel is a bird of prey. Do you know what this means? Look closely at its feet. Can you tell how it catches its food? How might its curved beak help it?

C Find these plants: tree of heaven (*Ailanthus altissima*), dandelion, milkweed, fleabane

The tree of heaven had buds on the ends of its branches all winter. What has happened to them?

Have you ever tried to dig up a dandelion? What did its root look like? Dandelions have tap roots that dig deep into the soil.

The milkweed is a perennial, a plant that comes back year after year. Can you think of other perennials?

The yellow center of fleabane looks like one flower but is really many tiny flowers. Each one makes a fruit and a seed. How does making lots of seeds help a plant?

What kinds of plants are weeds? Can you think of ways weeds are helpful?

D Find these animals: earthworm, sowbug, butterfly, ant, spider

Earthworms tunnel through the soil. How does this change the soil? How might these changes be good in a garden, but harmful in a native forest?

You may call sowbugs by a different name, like sowbugs or potato bugs. Where do they live?

The yellow butterfly just came out of its winter case. It is drying its wings before it flies away.

The boy is holding a beetle that is in the pupal stage. Sketch what it may look like as an adult.

What do ants eat?

These baby spiders hatched from eggs. Where were the eggs during the winter?

What is similar about all these animals? How are they different from mammals and birds?

Which things in the picture are part of nature and which are made by people? What would you like to change in this picture?

Summer Scavenger Hunt

A Find these animals: squirrel, dog, rat

How are these animals alike? How are they different?

The squirrel builds a nest of leaves in a tree. Do you know what a squirrel likes to eat?

Squirrels bury nuts for food in the winter. What happens to the ones they don't dig up?

What is the rat eating? What can we do to keep rats away?

How should dog owners care for their pets? What can happen when dogs run loose?

What other animals live in the city?

C Find these plants: tree of heaven, evening primrose, milkweed, ground ivy

Tree of heaven grows almost anywhere. How would you define the word "tree"?

What is the white fuzzy ball on the dandelion? What would happen if you blew on it?

Evening primrose is the tall yellow flower. Why do you think the word "evening" is in its name?

Milkweed is the pink-flowered plant. Why do you think it has this name?

Ground ivy is the tiny plant with purple flowers. It has several other names, including creeping Charlie and gill over the ground. Why can this plant survive in the city while some cannot?

Can you identify other plants that grow in your neighborhood?

B Find these birds: American Robin, House Sparrow, European Starling

How are birds different from other animals? How are they like other animals?

American Robins build nests of mud, grass and twigs. Where would you look for their nests? What is the robin feeding its young?

Using its name as a clue, where would you look for a House Sparrow nest?

European Starlings eat almost anything. Using this bird's name as a clue, do you think it is native to North America? Are there other birds that look like starlings that are native?

What kinds of birds have you seen in your neighborhood?

D Find these animals: earthworm, sowbug, Monarch butterfly, yellow sulphur butterfly, ant, spider, beetle

Does it surprise you to learn that the earthworms we see today, like the one the boy is holding, were brought to North America from Europe during colonial times?

Sowbugs are crustaceans, not insects. Name some other common crustaceans.

What do you observe on the milkweed leaf? This caterpillar will become a Monarch butterfly. The monarch butterfly is orange and brown.

The yellow butterfly is a yellow sulfur. What other insect is like a butterfly?

The black beetle eats caterpillars. Can you find any more insects in the picture?

Spiders are not insects either. How can you tell the difference between a spider and an insect?

What is similar about all these animals?

Which things in the picture are part of nature and which are made by people? What would you like to change in this picture?

Lauretta Jones

Fall Scavenger Hunt

A Find these animals: squirrel, opossum, bat

What is the squirrel doing? What did the squirrel use to build its nest? Fall is the time many animals prepare for winter.

How is the opossum's tail different from the squirrel's tail? It can use its tail like a hand and even hang by it. Female opossums carry their babies in a pouch on their bellies. Can you think of another animal that has a pouch?

Bats are the only flying mammals. At what time of day do they fly? What do they eat? Are bats helpful to us?

B Find these birds: American Robin, House Sparrow, Common Grackle

Why do you think you see so many birds in the fall? Do you know another season when you see many birds?

Can the American Robin find food in the winter? Will the robin stay here? Where will it go? When will it come back?

Can you tell what the House Sparrow is eating? Which plant might have provided its food? What else does it eat?

The Common Grackle is a native bird that resembles a non-native bird. Do you remember the name of this bird?

C Find these plants: tree of heaven (*Ailanthus altissima)*, milkweed, New England aster, goldenrod

How many plants in the picture are blooming?

Has the tree of heaven bloomed? How can you tell? What is happening to its leaves? Trees that lose their leaves are called deciduous. Can you name a tree that does not lose its leaves?

What is happening to the milkweed? Where did the pods on the stalk come from? What was in the empty milkweed fruit (pod)?

Count the blooms of the New England asters in the picture. Can you name another plant whose bloom looks like this?

The goldenrod plant fits its name. Where are the flowers of the goldenrod?

Fall is the end of this year's growing season. Where will new plants come from in the spring?

D Find these animals: beetle, butterfly, fly, ant, spider

How are the animals in this scene alike?

Monarch butterflies fly to a warmer place before winter. Some go to Mexico. What other animals migrate?

Can you see the pupa on the milkweed stem? It will become a yellow sulfur butterfly in spring.

The beetle on the ground is a ground beetle. Where do you think it's going?

Japanese beetles gather in groups. Do you know why?

Ants live and work together in groups. What different jobs do you think ants do?

Why are the flies swarming above the can? They lay eggs in dirty places like this.

How do spiders get ready for winter? Look closely for white cotton-like balls. What are they?

What changes may take place because the girl is picking up litter?

Which things in the picture are part of nature and which are made by people? What would you like to change in this picture?

Lauretta Jones

A

B

C

D

Winter Scavenger Hunt

A Find these animals: squirrel, rabbit

Find all the animal tracks. Can you identify the animals that made them?

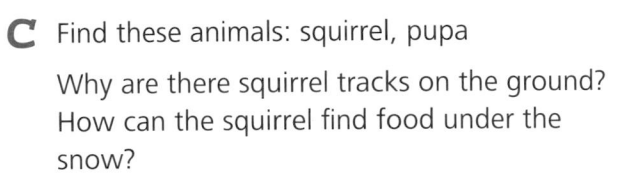

Rat tracks and squirrel tracks look like hands. How are rabbit tracks different from rat and squirrel tracks? Why are they different?

Where is the squirrel's home?

C Find these animals: squirrel, pupa

Why are there squirrel tracks on the ground? How can the squirrel find food under the snow?

Where do the insects and spiders that you see in the summer spend the winter?

How many different plants can you see in the picture? How are they spending the winter?

How do you know the tree of heaven is living? Where will next year's leaves come from?

 Do you recognize the milkweed pods? Where are the seeds now?

All of these plants produce thousands of fruits and seeds. How do these fruits and seeds help them survive in the city?

B Find these animals: Rock Pigeon, Northern Cardinal (male and female), House Sparrow

Find the American Robin's nest in the tree of heaven. Why isn't the robin in the picture?

How do birds keep warm in winter's cold?

Many Rock Pigeons live in the city. Some people don't like pigeons. Do you know why?

How can you tell the male Northern Cardinal from the female?

It is hard for birds to find food in the winter. If you choose to feed them, it is best to continue to do so throughout the season to help them survive the difficult weather conditions.

D What do wild animals drink when the water is frozen? What do they eat during the winter?

Look closely at the tracks at the bottom of the picture. What other mark identifies a rat track? Can you tell from the track in the picture where the rat lives?

Rats have no trouble finding food because people litter. Why should the girl in the picture be careful of the rat?

What are some survival strategies that mammals use to make it through the winter?

Can you find some animals that are at rest for the winter? The little cotton-like balls protect the eggs of spiders. The spider eggs are not ready to hatch until spring. In spring it is warmer, and there is food for baby spiders. What do baby spiders eat?

Which things in the picture are part of nature and which are made by people? What would you like to change in this picture?

General Resources

Canfield, Michael, R., ed., *Field Notes on Science & Nature.* Cambridge, CA: Harvard University Press, 2011.

Comstock, Anna Botsford. *Handbook of Nature Study.* Ithaca, NY: Comstock Publishing/Cornell University Press, 1986.

Cornell, Joseph Bharat, *Sharing Nature with Children.* 20th Anniversary Edition. Nevada City, CA: Dawn Publications, 1998.

Grubb, Thomas C. *Beyond Birding: Field Projects for Inquisitive Birders.* Pacific Grove, CA: The Boxwood Press, 1986.

Haupt, Lyanda Lynn. *The Urban Bestiary: Encountering the Everyday Wild.* New York: Little, Brown and Co., 2013.

Leslie, Clare Walker. *The Nature Connection: an Outdoor Workbook for Kids, Families, and Classrooms.* Pownal, VT: Storey Publishing, 2010.

Louv, Richard. *Last Child in the Woods: Saving Our Children from Nature-Deficit Disorder.* Updated and expanded ed. Chapel Hill: Algonquin Books, 2008.

Palmer, E. Lawrence and H. Seymour Fowler. *Fieldbook of Natural History.* New York: McGraw-Hill Book Co., 1975.

Sampson, Scott D. *How to Raise a Wild Child: the Art and Science of Falling in Love with Nature.* New York: Houghton Mifflin Harcourt, 2015.

Smith, Marilyn, et al. *The Kid's Guide to Exploring Nature.* Brooklyn: Brooklyn Botanic Garden, 2014.

Ward, Jennifer. *I Love Dirt! 52 Activities to Help You and Your Kids Discover the Wonders of Nature.* Boston: Trumpeter, 2008.

Wilson, Edward O. *Letters to a Young Scientist.* New York: Liveright Publishing Corporation, 2013.

Everyday Mysteries: Fun Science Facts from the Library of Congress: www.loc.gov/rr/scitech/mysteries/archive.html

Record Your Nature Observations: www.inaturalist.org/

Index